Basic Telephone Switching Systems

Basic Telephone Switching Systems

David Talley
Telecommunications Consulting Engineer

HAYDEN BOOK COMPANY, INC.
Rochelle Park, New Jersey

12 13 14 15 16 17 18 19   PRINTING

78 79 80 81 82 83 84 85   YEAR

Preface

Basic Telephone Switching Systems discusses, in a simplified manner, the basic principles of modern telephone switching systems. It covers the development of switching techniques from the early step-by-step dial central offices through the common-control electromechanical categories, as exemplified by the panel and crossbar types, to the present highly sophisticated electronic switching system.

The essential components of the various telephone switching systems and their modes of operation are effectively and simply explained. An important objective is to present a thorough understanding of the precepts of telephone switching, signaling, and transmission as well as related information storage, including path and trunk selection methods. The basic concepts of modern electromechanical and electronic switching systems are fully described. The reader also is able to follow the progress of a call through each of the step-by-step, panel, crossbar, and electronic switching types of central office.

The text has been presented in a manner that should be understood by those who do not have a formal engineering education. There is a minimum of mathematics. And the narration is concise and utilizes many related illustrations.

This book was written with the technician, advanced student, and engineer in mind. It is hoped that this treatment of an intricate subject will prove particularly helpful to personnel in the communications field, especially those responsible for the engineering, operation and maintenance of telecommunication services.

DAVID TALLEY

New York, New York

Contents

Basic Telephone Switching Systems

1

The Growth of Telephony

Growth of Telephone Communications

Dialing the telephone number of a neighbor or a friend in a distant city results in an immediate connection, hearing either a ringing or a busy signal. Few of us are aware of the complexities of that one connection. Dialing or pushbutton calling seven digits connects your phone with one of several million local lines; dialing ten digits connects your phone with nearly 115 million telephone stations across the North American Continent. Eventually by dialing 11 to 13 digits it will be possible to reach every telephone in the world. Such communications miracles are the result of complex electromechanical and electronic switching system developments.

The rapid growth of the telephone system has created additional communications requirements, leading to the development of sophisticated systems, such as teletype, facsimile, data, and television, using the telephone network.

In short, the growth of all communications media directly affects the growth of telephone switching systems. Figure 1-1 illustrates the growth of the telephone system during the past decade.

National Intertoll Network

The *direct distance dialing* (DDD) network, established by the Bell System, has made it possible to connect two telephones located almost anywhere in North America. The complex switching network that makes this possible is divided into primary, sectional and regional centers which serve a few hundred associated toll centers and about 22,000 end offices which serve subscribers. These centers automatically switch calls to one or more alternate routes when the direct, high usage routes are busy or not available.

Switching centers are interconnected by intertoll trunks, usually over 25 miles long, which use toll cables, coaxial cables and point-to-point micro-

1

Telephones In Service Throughout the World

Country	1959	1968	Percent increase
United States	66,645,000	103,752,000	55
Japan	4,334,600	18,216,767	320
United Kingdom	7,525,000	12,099,000	61
West Germany	5,090,100	10,321,281	103
Canada	5,122,500	8,385,476	64
Italy	3,182,500	7,057,187	121
France	3,703,600	6,999,621	89
WORLD	124,800,000	222,400,000	78

(From "The World's Telephones," AT&T 1968)

Figure 1-1

wave radio facilities. Carrier transmission is employed on almost all inter-toll trunks and increasingly on interoffice and tandem trunks. Figure 1-2 shows a simplified DDD network.

The several classes shown in this figure are used for traffic, transmission and other reference purposes. Calls between local central offices (class 5) in the same metropolitan area may be routed over interoffice trunks or through a tandem office. Calls between toll centers (class 4) follow the direct, high-usage routes where available. If these routes are busy, alternate connection routes through primary, sectional and regional centers are tried in that order.

The best means of explaining DDD routing is to follow a call from Los Angeles, California to New Haven, Connecticut. The calling subscriber in Los Angeles dials the area code (203) followed by the seven digits of the New Haven party. If high-usage trunks are available, the originating class 5 office in Los Angeles will route the call to the primary center serving that area. The switching equipment in that center will try to complete the call over the high-usage trunks marked 1, 2, and 3 in that order. If route 1 was not available and route 2 was busy, the call would be sent over route 3 to the sectional center in New York. This class 2 office would then switch the call via final route trunks through the primary and toll centers serving the New Haven area to the desired end office which would complete the connection to the called number.

If the trunks in the high-usage Los Angeles area were busy, the primary center would select route 4, the final route to the sectional center. The switching equipment would attempt to complete the call over routes designated A, B or C before using final route D to the regional center. Regional centers across the country are connected by direct trunks regardless of their geographical location. From the New York regional center, the call would be routed to New Haven through the sectional, primary, and toll centers to the desired end office as in Fig. 1-2.

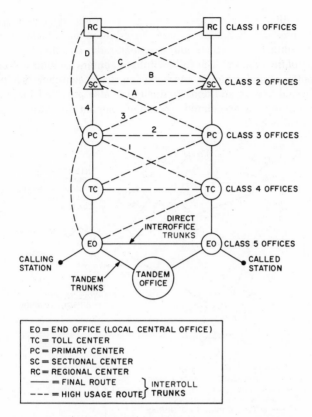

RC ┤ CLASS I OFFICES

SC ┤ CLASS 2 OFFICES

PC ┤ CLASS 3 OFFICES

TC ┤ CLASS 4 OFFICES

DIRECT
INTEROFFICE
TRUNKS

EO ┤ CLASS 5 OFFICES

CALLING
STATION

CALLED
STATION

TANDEM
TRUNKS

TANDEM
OFFICE

EO = END OFFICE (LOCAL CENTRAL OFFICE)
TC = TOLL CENTER
PC = PRIMARY CENTER
SC = SECTIONAL CENTER
RC = REGIONAL CENTER
——— = FINAL ROUTE   ⎫ INTERTOLL
– – – = HIGH USAGE ROUTE ⎭ TRUNKS

Figure 1 - 2   Simplified Direct Distance Dialing (DDD) Network

Elements of the Telephone System

The switching system of the class 5 office, (the central office), is the subject of this book. However, this system also forms the basis of the toll switching system (class 4 offices).

Figure 1 - 3 illustrates the basic elements of the telephone system and the associated toll connecting facilities.

Telephone instrument. The telephone instrument or station equipment, usually a rotary dial or pushbutton device, is used to initiate and receive calls.

Exchange outside plant. The exchange plant, composed of aerial and underground cables, connects telephone stations to central offices and interconnects central offices via interoffice trunks.

Central offices. The central offices contain the power supplies and the equipment for transmission, signaling, and related operations and the switching equipment for all interconnecting functions.

Toll plant. The toll plant includes the nationwide network of toll cables, coaxial cables and point-to-point microwave radio systems which connect the various toll switching centers in addition to submarine cables, satellite communication systems and overseas radio circuits.

Toll switching centers. The toll switching centers include toll centers, primary, sectional and regional centers comprising switching systems for the intertoll facilities. In addition, equipment is also provided for transmission, signaling and all associated operations similar to those performed by local central offices.

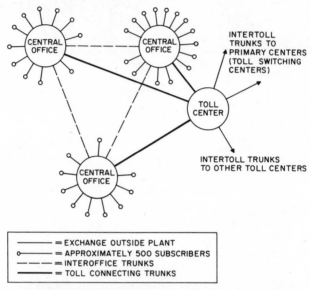

Figure 1-3   Elements of a Telephone System

Central Office Requirements

The growth of the telephone service in metropolitan and suburban areas across the country increased the need and therefore the number of central offices or exchanges. Approximately 11,000 central offices were required in 1968 to serve about 92 million telephones in the Bell System, and nearly 18 million subscribers were served by over 10,900 exchanges of independent telephone systems. Almost half of the Bell and independent exchanges are in small towns. In order to adequately serve the large number of telephones in large cities, several exchanges are housed in one central location.

Each central office or exchange has a theoretical capacity of 10,000 numbers. This capacity is based on the last 4 digits of the number, the first three being the designation of the exchange or central office. In a small locality having only one central office, there is no need to dial the first three digits. However, to conform to the requirements of nationwide direct distance dialing, each telephone station is assigned a seven-digit number.

Location of the Central Office

A telephone station is connected to its central office equipment by a pair of wires, commonly called the *tip* and *ring conductors,* which are contained in a multiconductor subscriber cable. The central office is usually located at the *wire center* of the subscribing telephones in order to efficiently use the exchange outside the plant. The wire center, a centralized location of wires from subscribing stations, is in a location designed to provide an efficient and economical distribution of wires and cables, see Fig. 1‑4.

Central offices are interconnected by trunk circuits, usually called interoffice trunks. Large cables, usually 19 or 22 gauge, are used for these trunk lines because of heavier transmission and signaling requirements. Along similar trunk lines, the central offices are connected to their assigned toll centers for direct distance dialing facilities.

Telephone Numbering Plans

The telephone numbering plan identifies each telephone station in any city or town. This address or identification (the telephone number) must be different from all others in the same service area.

In manual central offices, each operator had available 10,000 jacks appearing on the switchboard panels, representing one station per jack within the service area, since the numbers available to subscriber stations ranged in sequence from 0000 to 9999. In localities with more than one central office or exchange, each four-digit number was preceded by the name of its central office, often named after a locally historical personality.

This numbering plan continued with automatic switching, except that only the first three letters of the central office name were used for dialing purposes. Therefore Stuyvesant became STU and Spring became SPR.

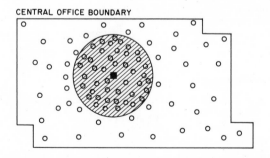

Figure 1‑4   Location of a Wire Center

In most localities the number of office codes, derived from the first three letters of the central office name, amounted to only 330 out of a possible 1000 (10 × 10 × 10) combinations. With rapid growth in telephone service, the use of easily pronounceable and geographically associated names was no longer feasible because of the limited number of useable words available for central office codes. As a result the 2 - 5 *numbering plan* was developed. The plan contained 2 letters and 5 numbers, substituting a numeral for a third letter, thereby increasing the capacity of the system.

With the development of the 2 - 5 numbering plan 64 combinations were possible for the exchange letters, although until substitute letters were added, some of the combinations were not acceptable. For instance 55 is a combination of a word whose first two letters are K, or J which is not possible. Development of this new numbering plan with substitute combinations created a total of 576 possible codes for central offices.

All-Number Calling Plan

In most metropolitan areas across the country, the demand for service proved too great for the 2 - 5 numbering plan. Letter office codes were no longer a feasible way of indicating exchange offices, except in small communities. Centrex switching, TWX service for teletype, and mobile telephones were creating an additional drain on the supply of available codes.

Capacities of Telephone Numbering Plan

Numbering Plan	Number of Useful Central Office Codes	Theoretical Number of Telephones in an Area. (based on 10,000 per code)
First three letters of central office name	330	3,300,000
2 - 5 Numbering plan	540	5,400,000
2 - 5 Numbering plan with arbitrary letter assignments	576	5,760,000
All-Number calling (202 codes of the 800 combinations (8 × 10 × 10) are reserved for use as Area Codes and for special purposes)	598	5,980,000

Figure 1 - 5

As a result of this unexpected growth, the letters in the 2 - 5 plan were replaced by numbers, creating the *all-number calling plan* or ANC. While certain number combinations were reserved, such as 411 for information and 911, the national emergency code for summoning police, the possible range of numerical combinations was greatly expanded and is not expected to need changes for a long time.

Numbering Plan Area Codes

By dialing 10 digits, the area code and a telephone number, a subscriber can be connected to almost any other telephone in the United States. Canada and parts of North America without operator assistance. Area code numbers, assigned to most parts of North America by the Bell System, consist of three numerals. The first digit does not contain 0 or 1, the middle digit is either a 1 or 0 and the last digit utilizes the numbers 1 to 9 and 0. This arrangement provides a total of 160 (8 $\times$ 2 $\times$ 10) possible area codes. The numerical distinction, 0 or 1, in the middle digit enables the common control switching equipment to distinguish a toll call from a local call.

The theoretical number of telephones in each numbering plan area as shown in Fig. 1 - 5 is 5,980,000. Approximately 152 area codes have been assigned to date. It is planned that some of the 598 three-digit codes, available under all-number calling (ANC), identifying central offices, also would be made available for future use as area codes. When it should become necessary to assign the same codes for this numbering plan as for central offices, new procedures for routing calls would be introduced.

World Numbering Zone Plan

World Numbering Zone Code	Zone or Region
1	North America including Hawaii, Central America and Caribbean Area except Cuba
2	Africa
3	Europe
4	Europe
5	South America and Cuba
6	Australia and South Pacific
7	USSR
8	North Pacific including Eastern Asia
9	Far East and Middle East

Figure 1 - 6

World Numbering Plan

With the advent of oceanic repeater-type telephone cables and communication satellites, international communications have greatly expanded leading to the eventual possibility of dialing calls on a world-wide basis. To provide for this, the International Telegraph and Telephone Consultative Committee (CCITT) of the International Telecommunications Union has proposed to divide the world into 9 numbering zones as shown in Fig. 1-6.

When available, a subscriber would be able, after first dialing an access code of two or three digits, to connect to the world network. The world numbering zone would then be dialed, followed by one or two digits of the code for the country except for North America which already has assigned area codes. Consequently, by dialing the 2- or 3-digit access code followed by a maximum of 11 to 12 digits, it would be possible to reach almost any telephone in the world.

Review Questions

1. By what percentage has the world's telephones increased in the past decade? What was the percentage growth in the United States?
2. What classifications of switching centers comprise the direct distance dialing network?
3. What are the intertoll trunk routing classifications? What is a class 5 office?
4. What are the main elements of a telephone system?
5. Approximately how many central offices were required in 1968 to serve all telephone stations in the United States?
6. What is the theoretical line capacity of a central office? What is the basis for this capacity?
7. Define a wire center.
8. Describe the two types of local telephone numbering plans in current use. How many useful central office codes can each provide?
9. What are numbering-plan area codes? What is the theoretical maximum number of codes available?
10. How many numbering zones is the world divided into for telephone dialing purposes?

2

Telephone System Concepts

Common-Battery System

Since the invention of the telephone, the design, manufacture and operation of switching systems has grown rapidly. In the early years of the telephone, engineering efforts concentrated on developing telephone instruments, aerial and underground cables, transmission techniques, and the common-battery system. The common battery, located in the central office, eliminated the need for a hand-cranked magneto and dry cell battery within each telephone unit.

Basic elements of the local battery telephone system are shown in Fig. 2-1. Cranking the magneto generated a low-frequency alternating current, operating a drop at the switchboard, which signaled the operator. The magneto was also cranked at the termination of a call as a disconnect signal. When the telephone was lifted off the receiver hook, the local battery circuit was completed, supplying *talking battery* to the carbon transmitter. The induction coil or transformer increased the resultant voice-frequency voltage for transmission over the telephone line. Today local battery operation has been almost entirely replaced by the common battery method except for military field telephone systems and other special applications.

In the common-battery system, the central office supplies a 24- or 48-volt storage battery for the talking battery as well as the power for signaling and ringing for all telephones. The power is supplied to individual telephones by one of two basic methods: the *bridged impedance* or *capacitor-inductor* arrangement or the *repeating-coil battery-supply* method, see Figs. 2-2 and 2-3.

The bridged impedance or capacitor-inductor circuit, used in the step-by-step and crossbar switching systems, furnishes the battery power to the subscriber loop through the windings of a relay with a high impedance to minimize transmission loss of voice frequencies. See Fig. 2-2. In addi-

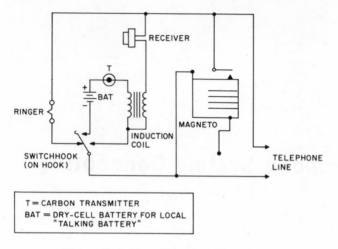

RINGER

RECEIVER

T

+
BAT
–

INDUCTION
COIL

MAGNETO

SWITCHHOOK
(ON HOOK)

TELEPHONE
LINE

T = CARBON TRANSMITTER
BAT = DRY-CELL BATTERY FOR LOCAL
      "TALKING BATTERY"

Figure 2-1   Local Battery Telephone

tion to serving as battery-feed inductors or retard coils, these relays respond
to the subscriber's switchhook signals and dial pulses. The capacitors, designated C, pass the voice currents around the relays.

The repeating-coil battery-supply circuit, Fig. 2-3, is often employed
in trunk circuits associated with step-by-step and panel dial offices. The
resistance lamp, R_L, protects the repeating coil from excessive current and
possible saturation on short loops. Repeating coils are transformers and
consist of two or more windings, each magnetically coupled to all other
windings. The voice signals are repeated from one circuit to the other usually without voltage or current changes by means of a 1 to 1 ratio of trans-
formation. In order to separate the voice currents from the common-battery supply, the supply is connected to the center of the repeating coil windings where the voice-frequency potential is nominally zero. Capacitor C
furnishes an additional path to bypass the voice currents around the central office battery supply.

Manual Telephone System

The switching system of the early manual telephone involved none
of the intricate electromechanical linkages of today. Interconnections of
subscriber lines were completed by young boys who joined the terminals
of the calling and called lines with jumper cables. The manual switchboard
replaced this awkward system with cords fitted with plugs at each end
which substituted the jumper wires.

In later developments of manual switchboard design, the subscriber
lines and trunk circuits were connected to jacks located on vertical panels.
Several pairs of cords, usually 17, were equipped with a three-conductor
plug and installed on the horizontal keyshelf. The plug connectors were
designated *tip* (T), *ring* (R) and *sleeve* (S). The tip and ring were the transmission leads. The sleeve served as the control lead and was also used to

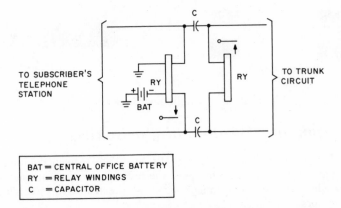

Figure 2-2   Bridged Impedance or Capacitor-Inductor
Common-Battery Supply in Central Office

make-busy the jack circuit into which the plug was inserted for a connection. See Fig. 2-4. Additional jacks completed connections between a calling line and an outgoing trunk to other central offices, increasing the capabilities of the system.

In larger cities, as the telephone system grew the switchboard was
divided into two parts. Originating traffic was handled by an A board and
incoming calls were handled by a B board. The separation of originating
and incoming calls permitted the A operator to serve just originating calls
faster and more efficiently.

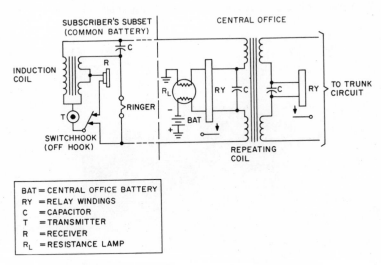

Figure 2-3   Repeating-Coil Common-Battery
Supply in Central Office

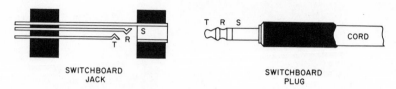

SWITCHBOARD
JACK

SWITCHBOARD
PLUG

Figure 2-4   Switchboard Jack and Plug

Development of Automatic Switching

While the development of automatic switching was accelerated by the rapid growth of metropolitan areas, the initial need arose in small communities where it was often unnecessary and uneconomical to employ 24-hour operators.

In large cities, automation became necessary because operators could no longer handle the large volume of calls. Complex electromechanical switching systems, first designed to aid and then later to replace operators, essentially simulate the operations of the plugs and jacks on a manual switchboard with only a few exceptions. The following sequence of processing a local call will serve to illustrate the similarities.

1. Switchboard panels are scanned for lights indicating a demand for service.

2. A lamp lights; location and identity of call is recorded.

3. An answering cord is inserted and the word "operator" is spoken.

4. Identification of the calling line is received and recorded.

5. A jack of the called line is located.

6. The condition of the called line is determined by testing the jack with the tip of the calling cord.

7. A connection is completed if the called line tests idle.

Figure 2-5   Electromechanical Switching Relay

courtesy of Automatic Electric Co.

8. If the called line tests busy, the calling subscriber is informed.

9. The operator releases the cord circuit after the connection is completed, and is then available to handle another call.

10. Condition of the call in progress is observed via lamps on a keyshelf associated with the cord circuit.

11. The connection is released when lamps signal that both parties have disconnected.

The direct interconnections on manual switchboards are not easily adaptable to automatic control. It is often necessary for mechanical switching devices to make a connection from one terminal to any one of a number of other terminals through the use of relays and mechanical motions of metallic contact elements. Moving brush-type selector switches, rotary or stepping switches and crossbar switches are examples of the devices that complete these interactions. Figures 2-5 and 2-6 show two types of switching devices and Fig. 2-7 illustrates the operation of a stepping switch.

Figure 2-6   Electromechanical Stepping Switch

courtesy of Automatic Electric Co.

Switching System Classifications

Electromechanical switching systems provide the means of interconnecting on demand a particular set of transmission paths. These paths permit a calling subscriber to communicate with any other subscriber in the public telephone network. Two main classifications of electromechanical switching systems have been developed. They are (1) the step-by-step and (2) the common control systems.

The step-by-step system is a direct, progressive control system in which the selecting switches are directly controlled by the pulses generated by the dialing of a number. The dialed information is registered by the interconnecting switches. For example, if the digit 7 is dialed, the particular selector switch will be advanced seven times or stepped to its seventh level. Figure 2-8 shows the main elements of the direct control step-by-step automatic switching system.

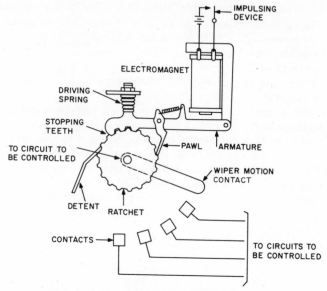

Figure 2-7   Stepping Switch Operation

In the common-control switching systems, dial pulses usually are recorded in a register-sender unit of the central office switching equipment. Computer-type circuitry using relays, switches and electronic equipment perform the switching functions. Common-control operations also may be applied to step-by-step as shown in Fig. 2-9. The link circuit first connects the *linefinder* and *first selector* to the *register-sender control* circuit. Upon completion of all selections, the link circuit disconnects the register-sender control circuit and interconnects the linefinder and first selector circuits.

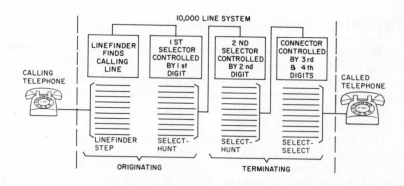

Figure 2-8   Direct-Control Step-By-Step Switching System

Telephone Station Apparatus

The telephone instrument, or *subset,* is used to signal the central office equipment. It is composed of a transmitter, receiver, ringer, switchhook, rotary dial or pushbuttons, and an electrical transmission network. The network separates the transmitter and receiver circuits. The telephone performs the following functions:

1. Signals the central office equipment that a call has been originated, answered, or disconnected.

2. Alerts the subscriber to an incoming call by ringing.

3. Transmits a called number to the central office switching equipment.

4. Converts speech to electrical energy and vice versa.

5. Provides for full duplex (simultaneous transmission and reception) operations over a two-wire circuit.

Telephone sets and their assigned central offices are designed for either two- or four-wire operation. Two-wire circuits carry voice signals in both directions simultaneously over a single pair of wires. Four-wire circuits contain separate wires for each direction of transmission. Because of the economic advantage of using only a single pair of wires, two-wire circuits

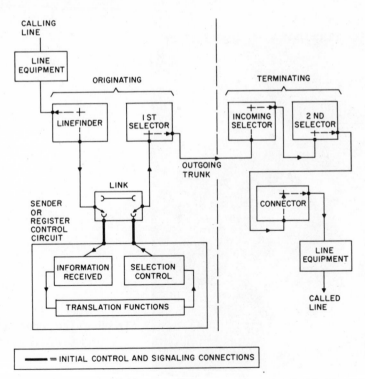

Figure 2-9   Common-Control Switching as Applied to the
Step-By-Step System

Figure 2-10   The 500-Type Telephone Set
courtesy of AT&T

**Figure 2-11
"Trimline" Telephone Set**
courtesy of AT&T

are used for connections to subscriber stations and local trunks. Four-wire circuits are used in almost all toll and long distance trunks that use carrier or multiplex facilities, and are increasingly used in inter-office, tandem and short-haul toll operations. Recent developments in carrier systems, particularly of the pulse code modulation (PCM) category, such as the type T1, have made the economic use of carrier facilities possible for such purposes.

Figures 2-10 and 2-11 are examples of two modern telephone models, the 500 model and the trimline. The trimline model (Bell Telephone ®) has the dial in the handset, lights when it is lifted, and has a "recall" button near the dial which when touched allows another call to be made without hanging up.

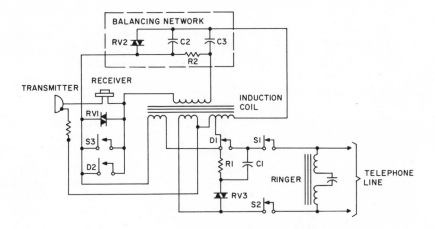

Figure 2-12   The 500-Type Telephone Schematic

Figure 2-12 is an elementary schematic of the 500 model set. Switches S1, S2 and S3 are components of the switchhook shown in the off-hook position. D1 and D2 are parts of the dial in its normal state. When the dial, for example, is pulled off-normal to number 4, and then released, the contacts of D1 will be opened and closed four times as the dial returns to its normal position. D2 at the same time is closed to short circuit the receiver to prevent the clicks from being heard.

RV1, RV2, and RV3 are semiconductor rectifiers called varistors. RV1 suppresses dial pulse clicks in the receiver. The balancing network, composed of varistor RV2, resistor R2, and capacitors C2 and C3 with the windings of the induction coil, form a hybrid arrangement which provides full duplex operation over a two-wire circuit. C1 and R1 make up a dial pulse filter to suppress high-frequency interference to nearby radio receivers. Varistors RV2 and RV3 with R1 also reduce the efficiency of the transmitter on short loops from the central office to maintain satisfactory transmission volume.

Signaling and Addressing Developments

On manual switchboards, the operator depended upon verbal instructions and lamp signals associated with corresponding cords and tone signals for the handling of calls. Despite the technical advances in processing calls, the need remained for the subscriber to transmit verbally the called number to the operator.

With the advent of electromechanical switching equipment, simple but reliable signaling had to be provided for communications between the subscriber and the equipment and between the various types of equipment itself. Development of the rotary dial and the more recent pushbutton method resulted in address signals for directly instructing the automatic equipment.

The Rotary Dial

The introduction of the rotary dial around 1895 marked a major advance in telephony. The dial, a device which rotates back to its stop position from a number or letter to which it was turned, opens and closes contacts as it turns, generating a train of d-c pulses corresponding to the number of the selected digit. These pulsed digits are used to directly position switches in the associated automatic central office.

Rotary dials, see Fig. 2-13, in telephone sets generate pulses at the rate of 10 per second, regardless of the digit dialed. Switchboard dials of private branches or automatic exchanges (PBX or PABX) may send 20 pulses per second, reducing operating time on these boards. Dials at toll or other switchboards associated with central offices or switching centers have been replaced by a keyset composed of a series of nonlocking keys; one for each decimal digit plus certain control keys. This keyset connects with the central office equipment and normally produces multifrequency (MF) tones.

Pushbutton dialing, rapidly replacing the rotary dial in subscriber's sets, utilizes a series of 12 pushbuttons instead of a rotary dial.

Pushbutton Dialing

Key pulsing, a form of pushbutton calling using multifrequency tones, has been used on toll and dial service assistance (DSA) switchboards for many years. It was never adapted, however, to consumer telephones because the system required proper filter circuits to guard against voice interference.

With higher switching speeds of electronic switching systems, the need for more rapid and accurate means of customer dialing has increased. The Bell System, as a result, developed a pushbutton dialing method which utilized developments in solid-state circuitry. Touch Tone ® dialing, using multifrequency tone keying, can send a-c pulses to the central office equipment or to other associated equipment such as a computer. Services of this sort are not possible with the rotary dial since the d-c pulses can only control the local central office equipment. The tones generated by Touch

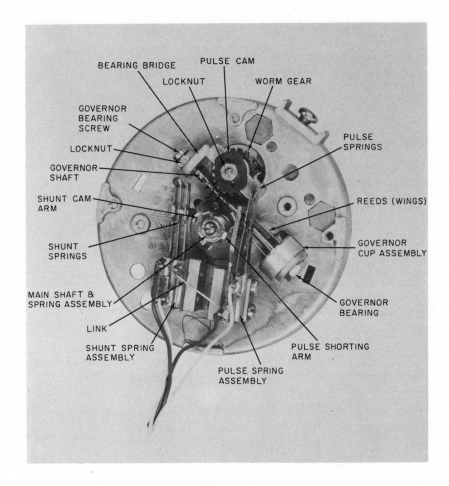

Figure 2 - 13   Rotary Dial Mechanism

courtesy of Automatic Electric Co.

Tone dialing, however, are in the voice frequency range and can be transmitted nationwide or worldwide, extending to the consumer new commercial services. For instance, a subscriber may be able to dial the number of an automatic supermarket and place an order by dialing a coded grocery list. Figure 2 - 14 shows a pushbutton set.

Eight frequencies in the 700- to 1700-Hz range comprise the four-by-four code designed for pushbutton dialing. The 8 frequencies, selected to avoid harmonically related interference from speech signals, are divided into 4 low-band and 4 high-band tones as illustrated in Fig. 2 - 15. Pressing a pushbutton results in the generation of 2 tones, a high-band and a low-band frequency. Pressing number 8 (TUV), for instance, causes the generation and transmission of 852- and 1336-Hz frequencies. For the 10 pushbuttons corresponding to the 10 holes in the rotary dial, only 10 frequency

Figure 2-14   Touch-Tone ® Telephone Set

courtesy of AT&T

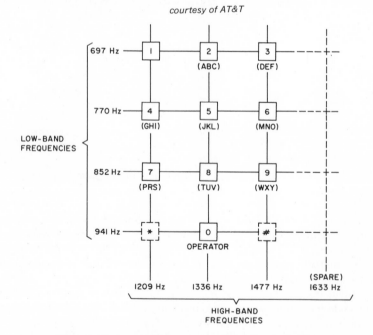

Figure 2-15   Pushbutton Dialing Frequencies

Pushbuttons having (*) and (#) are only equipped
for use with electronic switching offices or certain
specialized functions.

combinations are required. A four-by-three code would be adequate, omitting the 1633-Hz frequency.

The faceplate of the pushbutton set, see Fig. 2-16, is planned for a capacity of four rows and four columns, or 16 possible pushbuttons. However, three rows and four columns are currently all that is needed; ten for the digits 1 to 0 and two for special functions designated by * and # which are used primarily with electronic switching offices.

The Bell pushbutton telephone sets employ inductor-capacitor (LC) resonant circuits to generate the required tone frequencies. Recent electronic developments have introduced the use of integrated circuits, reducing the 15 components in the inductor-capacitor network to six.

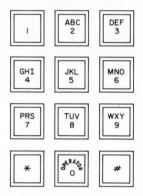

Figure 2-16
Faceplate of Pushbutton Telephone Set

Generation of Pushbutton Dialing Tones

In the Touch Tone® telephone set (inductor-capacitor network), pressing a pushbutton causes the rotation of two rods. One rod is associated with a row of pushbuttons and the other with a column. The pushbutton that is pressed determines which pair of rods will be rotated, resulting in the generation of two audio tones.

In Fig. 2-17, a 500-type telephone unit is shown, equipped for pushbutton dialing with the frequency generation unit which includes two tuned circuits. Each circuit consists of an inductance coil of the *ferrite cup core* type, which has three windings and a capacitor. The windings are designated L1A, L1B, L1C and L2A. L2B, L2C for the two inductors. Capacitor C1 is associated with inductor L1A and C2 is associated with L2A. Taps on the coil L1A are connected to the four rods linked with the rows of pushbuttons. The tuned circuit of L1A and C1 controls the generation of the lowband frequencies. Similarly, taps on L2A are associated with the three rods corresponding with the columns of pushbuttons. L2A and C2 form the tuned circuit to produce the highband range of pushbutton tones.

The operation of any pushbutton activates sets of contacts on switches K1, K2, and K3. One set of contacts on K1 is connected with each rod of the rows of pushbuttons. The contacts of K2 connect to the rods linked with the columns. K3 is common to all pushbuttons and is activated only during the latter part of the sequence of events. In the normal position of K3, most of the direct current drawn by the transmitter T will flow through RV1. Some current will also pass through L1A and L2A.

Assume that pushbutton 2 (ABC) has been pressed. The rod linked with the first row will close the contacts of K1. At the same time, the rod of the second column will close the contacts of K2. Activation of the contacts of K1 connects C1 to the first tap on L1A. Similarly, the operation of K2 connects C2 to the second tap on L2A, establishing the tuned or resonant circuits for producing the 697- and 1336-Hz frequencies. These frequencies correspond to the pressed digit 2 (ABC) but the tone signals have not yet been generated by the action of K3.

Not until the pushbutton is pressed all the way down does K3 operate, interrupting the direct current flowing through L1A and L2A, causing shock excitation of the two tuned circuits, and thereby generating the 697- and 1336-Hz frequencies. At the same instant, the central office battery voltage on the subscriber's line will be connected to transistor Q1, sustaining the 697- and 1336-Hz oscillations. The speech circuit in the telephone set will be shunted by the action of K3, but the subscriber will be able to hear the outgoing tone signals at a low level.

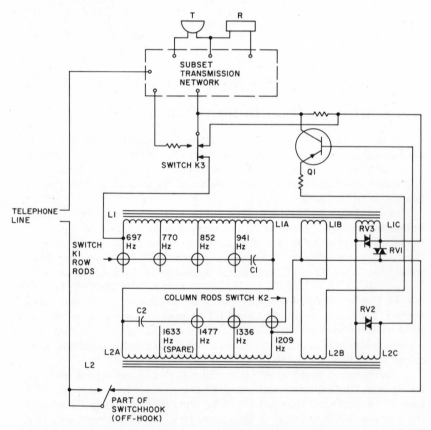

Figure 2-17   Pushbutton Dialing Telephone Set

Additional equipment is needed at the central office for handling the pushbutton signals. Two principal types of receivers have been developed for use in existing electromechanical offices. One converts the tone signals into direct-current dial pulses for operation of step-by-step and similar equipment, and the other signal detector translates the tone signals into a form which can be used by the common-control switching equipment. The pushbutton tone receiver and adapter units in central offices are designed to operate from both rotary dial and pushbutton sets.

Subscriber Line Circuit

In both manual and electromechanical switching systems, every subscriber line connects directly to an individual line circuit in the central office equipment. This circuit normally consists of two relays: the line (L) and cutoff (CO) relays. The windings of relay (L) are in series with the telephone line or loop to the subscriber's station. Whenever the handset is lifted to originate a call, contacts on the switchhook close a circuit to operate (L) which is the first indication to the switching equipment that a call is about to be initiated.

Figure 2-18 is a partial schematic of a typical subscriber line circuit applicable to step-by-step, panel, and rotary type switching systems. Note that the circuit for the operation of (L) is through the normally-closed contacts of (CO). If relay (CO) should be operated on an incoming call (L) cannot operate. And when (CO) operates in the first stage of an outgoing call, (L) will release.

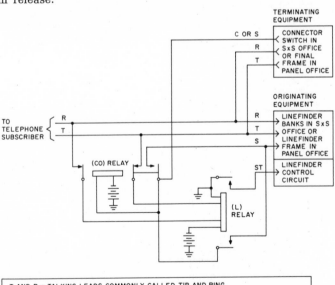

T AND R = TALKING LEADS COMMONLY CALLED TIP AND RING.
S = MAKE-BUSY CONTROL LEAD.
C = MAKE-BUSY CONTROL LEAD ASSOCIATED WITH CONNECTOR SWITCH IN SxS OFC.
SxS = STEP-BY-STEP CENTRAL OFFICE.

Figure 2-18   Typical Subscriber-Line Circuit Used in Step-By-Step and Panel Central-Dial Offices

On an originating call, the operation of relay (L) usually causes the following actions:

1. It connects battery potential through the normally-closed contacts of the (CO) relay to mark the calling line's position on the linefinder banks.

2. It grounds the ST or linefinder control lead to start a linefinder selector hunting for the calling line.

3. It prepares a circuit to make-busy the calling line to other calls. When the linefinder selector connects to the calling line terminals on the linefinder bank, the (CO) relay will be operated, removing (L) from across the subscriber's line and will make-busy the calling line to incoming calls by extending the ground condition on the S lead to the terminating equipment. The release of the (L) relay will remove the ground state from the ST lead to free the linefinder control circuit.

In the crossbar system, Fig. 2-19, a line relay is provided for each subscriber's line but individual (CO) relays are not needed. Contacts on the hold (LH) magnet of the crossbar switch and the crossbar switch contacts of the particular line number are used instead of a cutoff relay. In addition, in the crossbar system, each subscriber's line has only one appearance on a specific line-link frame. This assignment serves for both originating and terminating calls. Other electromechanical switching systems to be studied later need two separate line appearances; one for originating calls and another for terminating calls.

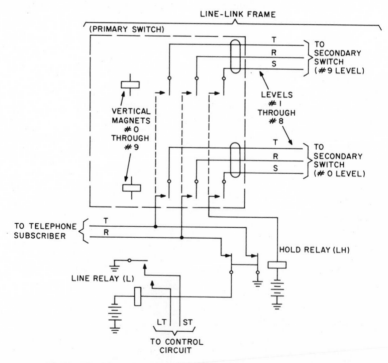

Figure 2-19   Crossbar System Subscriber-Line Circuit

Electronic switching offices (ESO) equip each subscriber line with a *ferrod senser*, an inductor which may be considered as a type of subscriber line circuit. Every ferrod senser is scanned about five times per second by the central control equipment to check its state, that is, whether it is on-hook or off-hook. When the handset is lifted to originate a call, increased direct current will flow through the coils of the ferrod senser, changing its state by affecting the pulses normally sent by the ferrod senser indicating an off-hook condition. The electronic equipment will then process the call.

Review Questions

1. What types of battery supply systems are used with telephone stations? Briefly describe their functions.
2. What are the two principal switching components in the manual switchboard?
3. What functions are performed by the tip, ring and sleeve conductors in a manual switchboard?
4. What main factors initially brought about the development of automatic switching systems?
5. What are the main classifications of electromechanical switching systems? How do they differ?
6. What are the chief categories of present common-control switching systems?
7. What are the basic components of a subscriber telephone instrument or subset?
8. Define two-wire and four-wire circuits and explain how they are used.
9. What are the advantages of pushbutton dialing? What frequencies are utilized?
10. What relays are associated with each subscriber line in a step-by-step central office?

3

Conveying Switching Information

Switching Information Categories

The address information, registered by the dial pulses or pushbutton tones of a telephone, establishes the basis for the subsequent operations of the switching equipment throughout the complex system of central offices, tandem and toll centers, primary, sectional and regional centers.

Switching information represents a variety of categories: the last four digits of a line number, digits of a long distance call, information on a switch location of a central office trunk, or signals requesting a check on a line to test if it is idle or not. In most cases, this information can be reduced to two-state signals; a yes or no condition, an on-off current flow, or an open or closed relay contact.

The origin and destination of two-state signals, sent or received, may be between a subscriber station and a central office or completely within or between central offices. In responding to transmitted information, the switching equipment in common-control systems first translates or reevaluates it and then routes it along a complex series of electromechanical interactions. Upon completion of a connection, the control equipment continues to collect additional information from its interconnecting units, establishing further connections or starting a new train of switching operations.

Subscriber Signaling

In addition to the signals required for switching equipment, there are two other general signal classifications: signals normally transmitted and received over subscriber loops via the central office and signals between central office switching centers. See Fig. 3-1.

The signals transmitted over subscriber loops can be subdivided into three groups: information, supervisory and control signals.

Information signals. Information signals are audible tones in the voice frequency range. They convey information to the customer or operator on the progress of a call. The ringing of a subset bell indicates that the line is being called or a busy tone indicates that the called line is busy.

Supervisory signals. Supervisory signals are requests for service. Lifting the handset will send an off-hook signal, indicating origination of a call. Replacing the handset will send the on-hook signal indicating disconnection. The flow of direct current from the central office over the subscriber loop provides the power for this type of signaling.

Control signals. Control signals are required for completing connections. The subscriber's dial originates signals by interrupting the flow of direct current and the pushbutton set generates tone signals.

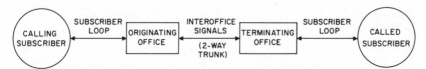

Figure 3-1   Subscriber-Loop and Interoffice Signaling Connections

Audible Information Signals

Audible information signals are standardized tones designed for easy interpretation by both operators and subscribers. They are produced by tone alternators in the central office and are used alone or in combination, depending on the signal required. A *high tone* is produced by an alternating current of 480 Hz. The *low tone,* produced by alternating current of 480 Hz, is modulated by a 620-Hz frequency to produce a low pitch. *Battery* or *battery* and *ground pulses* are direct current supplied by the central office battery, interrupted at rates of 30, 60, or 120 interruptions per minute (IPM).

Figure 3-2 lists the more important audible information signals of particular interest to subscribers and operators.

Supervisory Signals

Supervisory signals, activated by the switchhook of the telephone instrument, indicate to the central office that the subscriber wishes to originate, answer or disconnect a call. This two-state signaling device is designed to indicate four possible conditions.

Normal or inactive state. The normal state exists when the subset is on-hook and is not connected with a talking path in the central office.

Calling state. The calling state is indicated by an off-hook signal, but with no talking path connecting the telephone with the central office.

Talking state. The talking state is an off-hook condition but the talking path through the central office is connected.

Disconnection or release. Disconnection is indicated by an on-hook signal while connected to a talking path in the central office.

Supervisory signals are originated before or after conversation has been established. The direct current flowing in the subscriber loop is used for supervising as well as furnishing power to the transmitter in the subscriber's subset. Since it is necessary to prevent interference between supervisory and voice currents, supervisory signaling systems are carefully designed so that voice currents will not cause false operations.

Principal Types of Audible Information Signals

Designation	Function	Composition
Dial Tone	Informs subscribers they may start to dial.	High tone = 480 Hz
Audible Ringing or Ringback Tone	Called line has been reached and ringing has started.	440 Hz modulated by 480-Hz tone.
Line Busy Tone	Called line was reached but it is busy.	Low tone interrupted at 60 IPM, 50% break.
All Trunks Busy (ATB), Reorder or Overflow Tone	Local switching paths busy or eqpt. in central ofc. serving called subs. busy.*	Low tone interrupted at 120 IPM.
No Circuit (NC) Tone	No intertoll circuit is available.**	Low tone interrupted at 30 IPM.
Vacant Code Tone	Office code dialed is not assigned. Denotes vacant level in SxS offices.	Low tone interrupted at 60 IPM, 50% break, with each third tone pulse omitted.
Reverting Tone	Called party is on same party-line. Calling party to hang-up while line is rung.	Low tone interrupted at 60 IPM, 50% break. Same signal as "Line Busy Tone."

* = This signal also may be used to indicate that an unassigned office code was dialed.
** = Used on nationwide dialing or DDD calls.

Figure 3-2

Figure 3-3 shows a common method of subscriber loop supervision as used in crossbar and step-by-step offices. The figure shows only the supervisory relays, operational for a completed call state. Reverse battery supervision, to be discussed later, is used for the trunk circuit between the originating and terminating central offices. Note that in the originating office, relay (SA) is controlled by the switchhook of the calling subscriber station. Similarly, the operation of relay (SB) in the terminating office is under the control of the switchhook of the called party. Therefore, if either party hangs up, the respective supervisory relay will release and the call will be disconnected.

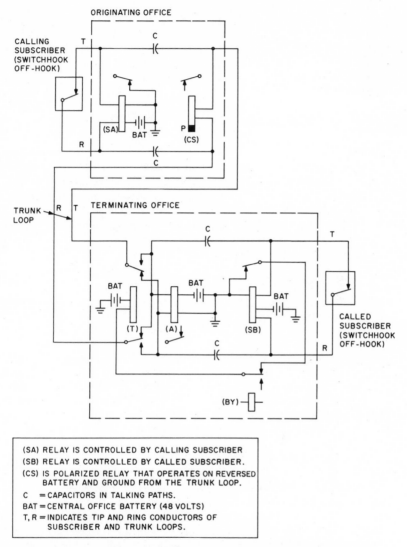

(SA) RELAY IS CONTROLLED BY CALLING SUBSCRIBER
(SB) RELAY IS CONTROLLED BY CALLED SUBSCRIBER.
(CS) IS POLARIZED RELAY THAT OPERATES ON REVERSED
      BATTERY AND GROUND FROM THE TRUNK LOOP.
C   = CAPACITORS IN TALKING PATHS.
BAT = CENTRAL OFFICE BATTERY (48 VOLTS)
T, R = INDICATES TIP AND RING CONDUCTORS OF
      SUBSCRIBER AND TRUNK LOOPS.

Figure 3 - 3   Subscriber-Loop Supervision on Completed Call

Control Signaling to Step-by-Step Offices

Dial pulses and pushbutton tones constitute the main types of control signals in subscriber loops. The subset dial, while returning to its normal position, opens and closes the subscriber loop. The number of open or *break* pulses (control signals) are equal to the digit dialed. If the digit 4 was dialed, there would be four break pulses produced. The loop is closed for a longer time between digits than between breaks of the dial pulses due to the interdigital pause in dialing. This longer pause called the *make* interval, enables the central office equipment to recognize the end of a digit and initiate control actions.

Trains of dial pulses are defined in make and break percentages and the rate of pulse repetition. The make pulse is a closed loop, off-hook state and the break interval is an open loop, on-hook state. The percent break interval of the dial pulse train is obtained by the formula:

$$\text{Percent break} = \frac{\text{break interval duration}}{\text{break + make intervals}} \times 100$$

Modern dials are designed for a 60 to 64 percent break interval. The pulse repetition rate of a subscriber dial is usually from 9 to 11 pulses per second, while certain operator dials used on PBX switchboards are capable of 20 pulses per second when used with suitable central office equipment. Figure 3-4 shows the train of dial pulses generated when digit 4 is dialed. Note that the ratio of the break to the make interval is about 60 to 40.

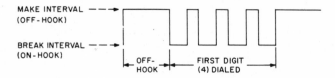

Figure 3-4   Control Signaling During Dialing

In step-by-step offices, dial pulses govern the operation of a control relay. The relay, in turn, controls the operation of its associated step-by-step switch or selector. Figure 3-5 illustrates a typical first selector circuit.

Relay (A) is held energized over the subscriber loop through the normally-closed contacts of the dial. Relay (B) is a slow release (SR) type, having a copper sleeve around one end of its iron core. Therefore, when (A) momentarily releases during the first break interval of the dial pulse, the current induced in the copper sleeve of (B) will keep it energized. At the same time that (A) momentarily releases, (C) and the vertical magnet (VM) of the selector will operate. Relay (C) is in series with the vertical magnet and both operate through the back contact of relay (A), during its initial release interval. The (C) relay is also slow release and will remain operated during the make intervals of the dial pulses for each digit. The vertical magnet raises the selector mechanism vertically in step with the break interval of each dial pulse. At the completion of the pulses, relay (C) will release because of the longer make interval between digits. This pause is due to the time required to pull the dial to the next numeral. The release of (C) allows the selector circuit to advance and initiate rotary motion in order to find an idle path or trunk. When this action has occurred, relay (D) will operate, cutting through the circuit to the succeeding selector in the switch train.

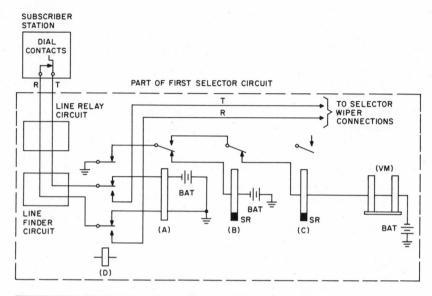

BAT = CENTRAL OFFICE BATTERY (48 VOLTS)
T   = TIP SIDE OF LINE } CONNECTED TO WIPERS OF SELECTOR.
R   = RING SIDE OF LINE }
SR = DENOTES SLOW RELEASE RELAY.
VM = VERTICAL MAGNET OF SELECTOR.
(A),(B),(C) AND (D) = RELAYS IN FIRST SELECTOR CIRCUIT. RELAYS
             (A),(B) AND (C) ARE OPERATED DURING
             MAKE INTERVAL OF DIAL PULSE

Figure 3-5   Control Signaling Functions in Step-By-Step Office

Control Signaling to Common-Control Offices

In common-control offices the dial pulses from the subscriber station do not directly govern the switching actions. The dial pulses or control signals are recorded and stored temporarily as they are generated. The stored information is then used to establish the necessary talking paths.

The equipment used for recording and storing the dial pulses in a crossbar office is called the *originating register* and in the panel type office, it is called the *subscriber sender*. Because of the dial pulse variations and distortions by the subscriber loop, a three-winding relay of the polar class is normally used as the line supervisory and pulsing relay, designated (L) in the originating register and subscriber sender circuits. The primary winding of relay (L) controls its operation. The secondary winding with capacitor C1 and resistor R1, as shown in Fig. 3-6, increases its operating speed. Current through the bias winding, however, causes a fast release action during the break interval of the dial pulse.

Relay (L) responds directly to the dial pulses, releasing with break intervals and closing with the make intervals. The break intervals are converted by (L) to ground pulses which actuate relays in the dial pulse counting circuit, to be discussed with the No. 5 Crossbar system.

In the relay (L) dialing circuit in Fig. 3-6, (L) is held operated over the subscriber loop by current flowing through the circuit formed by the primary winding, the ring coil of the dial tone transformer, subscriber loop, the closed dial contacts and back over the tip side of the subscriber loop to ground on the tip coil of the dial-tone transformer. (LA) and (SR) operate in series to the ground on the operated contact of (L). Relay (SR), a slow release type relay, will not open when (L) releases momentarily during dialing. However, it will drop and cause the release of the connection in case the customer should abandon the call by hanging up.

The momentary opening of the dial contacts during dialing will cause (L) and (LA) to release. The initial release of (LA) operates (RA) which is also a slow release relay. (RA) remains operated until (LA) stays operated for a longer time, usually 0.2 seconds or more, as at the end of a series of digit pulses. The release of (RA) sets up a circuit to record the num-

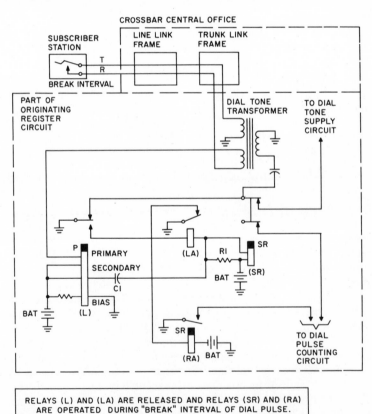

Figure 3-6   Control Signaling Operations in Common-Control Offices

ber of digit pulses in the *digit registering circuit,* and then prepares another circuit to register pulses of the next digit. Once the digit registering circuit has recorded the first digit, the dial tone is disconnected from the dial-tone transformer.

When pushbutton tone pulsing is provided at subscriber stations, tone receiver and converter circuits are installed to coordinate with the crossbar originating register or the subscriber sender in panel offices. The director type step-by-step office, designed for common-control operations, requires tone adapter and tone receiver circuits in the register-sender circuit. The pushbutton tone converter changes the two tones representing each digit into ground pulses used in the digit registering circuit. The net result is the same as the train of dial pulses received by the originating register.

Review Questions

1. Define address information. What is its usual form?
2. What type of signals can switching information be reduced to?
3. What are the two general classifications of information signals?
4. Define control signals. What device usually originates these signals?
5. Name three or more principal types of audible information signals.
6. What are subscriber supervisory signals? What actuating device usually is employed for these signals?
7. What is the normal state of the subscriber's instrument? What is the talking state?
8. How are trains of dial pulses usually defined? What is the normal dial speed?
9. What equipment records and stores dial pulses in common-control central offices?
10. What type of relay is used in the crossbar central office to respond to dial pulses?

4

Signaling Methods

Interoffice Signaling Systems

Gathered under the general term interoffice signaling are a variety of control and supervisory functions providing communication between central offices. Signals over trunk lines serve control operations by directing the seizing, holding and releasing of interoffice connections. The signaling system supervises trunk status by indicating the on-hook or off-hook condition of the called station switchhook. These conditions may also be called *far-end answer* and *far-end disconnect*. Address information is also conveyed by the signals in the form of dial pulses, revertive pulses or multifrequency tones.

Interoffice signaling systems may be divided into two categories: d-c signaling and a-c signaling. Direct-current signaling methods are used extensively for short distances, between local central offices, and for certain short haul toll trunks. Alternating-current signaling is used primarily with intertoll trunks and where d-c signaling is not economical or feasible. A-c signaling, for example, is used for trunks derived from carrier or multiplex channels.

D-C Loop Signaling Systems

Two general classes of d-c signaling methods have been developed and are known as *loop signaling* and *E and M or derived signaling leads*. Loop signaling, the simplest type, is most commonly used on local interoffice trunks. It is composed of metallic conductors of the trunk loop and terminating equipment with relays at each end of the trunk circuit.

Control and supervisory signals are generated by interrupting current flow, changing the value of the current or reversing the direction of the current flow at the far-end of the trunk. The current changes are detected at the other end of the trunk by various kinds of relays, such as the marginal and polar types. *Reverse-battery* and *battery-ground* d-c loop signaling methods are the most widely used. The *high-low* and *wet-dry* signaling methods were used with manual central-office switchboard trunks and have been replaced.

Reverse-battery Signaling

Modern electromechanical switching systems employ reverse-battery signaling for supervision and control of trunk lines between local and central offices. By operating on the principal of current flow reversal, this signaling system provides answering supervision, indicating when the called party has answered the call.

When an interoffice trunk is idle, a polarity exists on its conductors in crossbar and step-by-step offices with battery on the ring and ground on the tip conductors. During the progress of a call the trunk supervisory relays create the polarity. The battery and ground state of the trunk indicates to the originating central office that the subset of the called party is on-hook and ringing. When the party answers, the resulting off-hook signal causes the terminating office equipment to reverse the battery potential on the trunk towards the originating central office. With the indication that the called party has answered, the switching equipment completes the talking path. Where message rate service is furnished, the reverse-battery answer supervision will close through circuits for recording the call or for operating the calling subscriber's message register.

Figure 4-1 illustrates reverse-battery signaling as applied to interoffice trunks between step-by-step offices. Crossbar offices employ similar circuits, as shown in Fig. 3-3.

In Fig. 4-1 all loop pulsing has been completed and connections have been established between the called line terminals by the terminating office equipment. Relay (A) in the originating office is held operational over the calling subscriber's loop circuit through the normally-released contacts of (D). Relay (A) furnishes talking battery to the calling subscriber's subset and closes a circuit from ground on one of its operated contacts to operate (B). With (B) operational, the secondary winding of the polar type (C) relay is energized but does not operate at this time.

When the primary winding of (C) is energized it is connected across the outgoing trunk conductors through the make contacts on (A) and (B). Tracing back through the trunk loop to the connecting circuit in the terminating office, note that there is ground on the tip and battery potential on the ring conductors coming from the (CA) relay. The (CD) relay is not operational because the called subscriber's handset is still on-hook.

Relay (C) in the trunk circuit is a polar relay containing two coils which are designated primary and secondary windings. These coils are placed on opposite sides of the magnetic circuit of the relay, allowing it to operate only when the current flows in the same direction through both windings. Consequently, as long as (CD) in the terminating office is not operational, the battery on the ring and ground on the tip of the trunk loop will cause the current flowing through the primary winding of (C) to be in the opposite direction than the current flowing in its secondary winding. (C) cannot operate under these conditions.

When the subscriber answers, the off-hook condition operates relay (CD) in the connector circuit, reversing the direction of the current flowing from the windings of (CA) over the trunk loop to the originating office. (CD) is equipped with make-before-break contacts to prevent the interruption of current flowing through the windings of (CA). Therefore (CA) will not release during this transfer of battery and ground polarities. The trunk loop will now have battery on the tip and ground on the ring conductors. As a

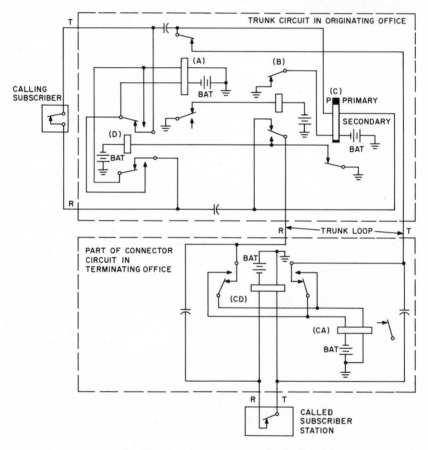

T, R = TIP AND RING CONDUCTORS
BAT = CENTRAL OFFICE BATTERY (48 VOLTS)
(A), (B), (C) AND (D) = RELAYS IN ORIGINATING OFFICE TRUNK CIRCUIT
                        OPERATED ON ANSWER SUPERVISION.
(CA) AND (CD) = RELAYS IN TERMINATING OFFICE OPERATED WHEN
                CALLED SUBSCRIBER ANSWERS.

Figure 4-1   Reverse-Battery Signaling and Answer Supervision

result the current flowing through the primary winding of (C) will be in the same direction as in its secondary winding and the relay will operate.

The operation of (C) closes a circuit from ground on its make contacts to operate (D). Relay (D) then reverses the d-c polarity from the windings of (A) over the loop back to the calling subscriber station. (D), like (CD) in the connector circuit, is equipped with make-before-break contacts so that (A) will not release during this transfer of polarities. This current reversal in the calling subscriber loop, which places battery on the tip and ground on the ring, remains during the conversation period.

Battery-Ground Pulsing and Signaling

In step-by-step switching systems the subscriber dial pulses directly control the operation of the selector switches. It is possible, therefore, that the resistance of the trunk conductors between a number of central offices may be too high for satisfactory loop pulsing. The *battery-ground pulsing* technique is often used when this occurs.

This pulsing method, which requires no additional equipment, supplies battery and ground at the originating office of opposite polarity to the battery and ground furnished over the trunk loop from the equipment in the terminating office. By placing the battery supplies of two central offices in series, this battery and ground polarity system nearly doubles the current flow over the trunk loop and assures satisfactory operation of the selectors in the terminating office. Once the trunk loop pulsing has been completed, the battery and ground from the originating office are disconnected from the trunk.

In Fig. 4-2 relay (A) in the originating office releases and operates in unison with the dial pulses from the calling subscriber station. In turn, it causes relay (TC) in the outgoing trunk circuit to operate and release with the pulses, connecting battery and ground over the trunk loop to operate (CA) in the distant terminating office as follows: Battery through resistor R1 is sent over the tip of the trunk loop through the normally closed contacts of (CD) and then through one winding of (CA) to ground. Another contact on the (TC) relay closes ground through resistor R2 to the ring side of the trunk loop. This ground connects through the other winding of (CA) to the terminating office battery. The operation of (CA) serves to control its associated selector. Thus, the 48-volt batteries of the originating and terminating offices form a series connection. At the end of loop pulsing, the trunk circuit in the originating office will revert to the reverse-battery condition as in Fig. 4-1.

E and M Signaling Systems

The E and M system received its name from historical designations found on old circuit drawings. The E referred to the middle "e" in received and the M from the "m" in transmit. Long interoffice and short-haul toll trunks use this derived signaling method. Separate signaling apparatus is needed at the end of each trunk and the conductors connecting the equipment to the trunk circuit are termed the E and the M leads. Different lead arrangements may be used with both d-c and a-c signaling categories.

In the d-c E and M signaling category, duplex (DX), simplex (SX), and composite (CX) signaling systems are the most important, for they provide signaling and dial pulsing over greater distances than is possible with loop signaling. E and M signaling is used with the a-c methods of in-band single-frequency (SF) and out-of-band systems which will be discussed later. For all these systems, signals may be sent in both directions at the same time without mutual interference.

The E lead in this system is the signal receiving conductor which reflects the far-end condition of the trunk. Ground on the E lead indicates that a signal has been received from the other end. When the trunk is idle, that is when there is a no signal condition, the E lead is said to be open or not grounded. The M lead transmits the near-end condition of the trunk. It is grounded when the trunk is idle or whenever the near-end subscriber is on-hook, in which case no signal is sent. When the trunk is seized or when the called party goes off-hook, a battery potential is substituted for the ground on the M lead, transmitting a signal to the other end of the trunk. Figure 4-3 illustrates a variety of E and M lead conditions for signals sent over interoffice trunk circuits.

Duplex (DX) Signaling

Figure 4-4 presents the essential components of a trunk circuit arranged for DX signaling and also illustrates the basic operation for both a-c and d-c signaling categories.

When the trunk is idle, all relays shown are released. The E leads in both originating and terminating offices will be ungrounded or open and the M leads will be grounded through the normally-closed contacts of the (A) and (CS) relays. The polar (DXA) and (DXB) relays cannot operate at this time because both ends of their primary windings are connected to ground. Refer to Fig. 4-3 for the possible combinations of E and M lead conditions.

When the trunk has been seized in the originating office, relay (A) in the trunk circuit operates through the normally-closed contacts of (B) and by the closure of the T and R leads in the originating office equipment. With (A) operated, ground is removed and battery through a lamp resistance is connected to the M lead. This resistance battery potential is transmitted over the tip conductor of the trunk cable pair operating the (DXB) relay in the distant office signaling circuit. The (DXB) relay connects ground to the E lead in the terminating office as an indication that a signal has been received from the originating office. Relay (C) in the distant trunk circuit will be operated by the E lead ground, closing its contacts for the subsequent operation of the (CS) relay.

When the called party answers, the off-hook condition closes the operating path of (CS) in the far-end trunk circuit. The (CS) relay transfers the M lead from ground to resistance-battery polarity, reversing the direction over the tip of the trunk cable pair to operate polar relay (DXA) in the originating trunk circuit. Relay (B) operates by the ground on the make contacts

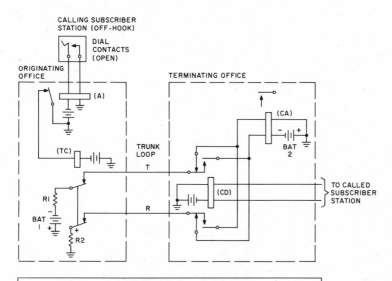

BAT 1 = BATTERY SUPPLY IN ORIGINATING OFFICE (48 VOLTS)
BAT 2 = BATTERY SUPPLY IN TERMINATING OFFICE (48 VOLTS)
RI,R2 = RESISTANCES IN SERIES WITH ORIGINATING-OFFICE BATTERY SUPPLY.
RELAY (TC) IN THE ORIGINATING OFFICE AND RELAY (CA) IN TERMINATING
   OFFICE ARE OPERATED WHEN DIAL PULSE IS TRANSMITTED.

Figure 4-2   Battery-Ground Pulsing and Signaling Circuit

E and M Lead Conditions for Trunk Signaling

Calling Subscriber or Trunk State	Originating Office		Direction of Transmitted Signal	Terminating Office		Called Subscriber State
	E Lead	M Lead		E Lead	M Lead	
Trunk Idle	Open	Ground	(none)	Open	Ground	On-Hook
Trunk Seized	Open	Battery	⟶	Ground	Ground	On-Hook
Off-Hook (Conversation Period)	Ground	Battery	⟵⟶	Ground	Battery	Off-Hook
On-Hook (Calling Subscriber Disconnects)	Ground	Ground	⟶	Open	Battery	Off-Hook
Trunk Disconnected	Open	Ground	(none)	Open	Ground	On-Hook

Figure 4-3

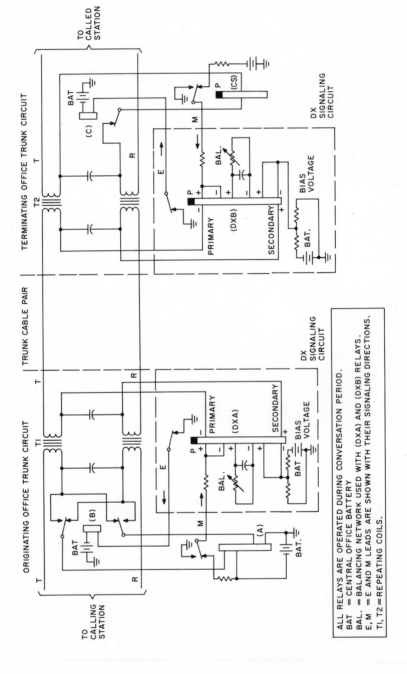

Figure 4-4   Duplex (DX) Signaling Circuit During Conversation Period

of the (DXA) relay which will reverse the battery and ground polarities from relay (A) as a signal to the originating office equipment that the called party has answered.

During the conversation period, both calling and called subscribers are off-hook and the M leads in the originating and terminating trunk circuits are connected to resistance battery as shown in Fig. 4-4. Both E leads will be grounded as relays (DXA) and (DXB) remain operated. Under ideal conditions no current will flow over the trunk conductors while an off-hook signal is sent simultaneously in both directions if the relays, associated components, and battery voltages in both central offices are equal. Because ground or earth return is employed with DX and similar systems, large distances between offices may result in ground potential differences and, to some extent, variations in central office battery voltages. The flow of current over the ring conductor of the trunk cable pair between the secondary windings of the polar (DXA) and (DXB) relays compensates for these variations.

When the calling party disconnects, the resulting on-hook signal releases relay (A) thereby grounding the M lead. This ground change over the tip conductor causes (DXB) to release, opening the E lead at the far-end trunk circuit. Relays (C) and (CS) also will release and the M lead in the distant trunk circuit will be grounded, effectively short circuiting the

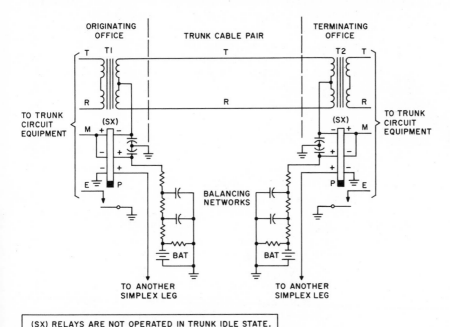

Figure 4-5   Simplex (SX) Signaling

primary winding of (DXA) which will release. The E lead at the near-end or originating trunk circuit will then be open. With the M lead grounded and the E lead open, an idle trunk condition exists.

Simple (SX) and Composite (CX) Signaling

Repeating coils and "dry" transmission (absence of battery and ground potentials) usually are employed on the longer trunk circuits to improve transmission performance. In such cases, dial pulses and supervisory signals cannot be transmitted over the trunk conductors in the same way as with "wet" trunks. The simplex SX circuit arrangement, Fig. 4-5, provides a simple method for signaling over dry trunks. The tip and ring trunk conductors are effectively in parallel so that the signaling range is much greater than with loop signaling. SX signaling can pass currents in either direction and will not interfere with voice transmission. However, the presence of earth potentials may limit operating range.

Composite CX signaling may be employed where SX signaling is not feasible, particularly if more than one d-c signaling path is needed for a trunk. Figure 4-6 illustrates the essential components. Two CX legs can be derived from one trunk pair. The CX set is composed of high-pass and low-pass filters arranged to separate the d-c and low-frequency signaling currents from the voice-frequency signals. The separation or crossover frequency is about 100 Hz. A CX set is required at each end of the trunk. Note that the composite path can only be used for d-c flow, it cannot be used for voice or other a-c transmissions. In some instances the SX path may be employed with CX signaling on a trunk in which case the simplex path alone may be used for voice frequency or other a-c transmissions but not for d-c purposes.

Alternating-Current Signaling Systems

A-C signaling systems are used on all intertoll circuits, and interoffice and short-haul toll trunks derived from carrier facilities. The trunk control, supervision of trunk status, and the dial pulsing generally can be handled by two-state signaling. For the revertive address function associated with panel switching offices, including trunk control and status signals, three-state a-c signals may be required. MF pulses for conveying dial pulsing are used extensively with the various two-state trunk control and status signaling systems. MF (multifrequency) signaling will be discussed later.

Signaling systems utilizing frequencies in the voice-frequency range of 200-3200 Hz are referred to as *in-band* or voice-frequency signaling. Since voice and signaling paths are the same for in-band systems, mutual interference must be prevented; the signal receiving equipment in particular must be protected to avoid false operation from speech sounds because it remains in operation during coversation in order to respond to signaling indications. *Out-of-band* signaling utilizes frequencies outside the voice-frequency band, usually in the 3400-3700 Hz range, thereby avoiding speech interference. It also permits the use of higher signaling tone levels.

The principal in-band signaling system in common use is the single-frequency (SF) type. It utilizes a standard frequency of 2600 Hz in both directions for trunks operating on a four-wire basis. For two-wire operation, two frequencies must be provided, 2600 Hz in one direction and 2400 Hz in the other, because the same two-wire transmission path is used between terminals.

The d-c signals received from the trunk equipment are translated into 2600-Hz tones for transmission over the voice channel. At the distant end, the received tones are converted to d-c signals. Normally voice and signaling frequencies are not on the trunk or voice channel at the same time. The equipment required for handling in-band signaling is needed only at the originating and end terminals, not at any intervening central offices. The speech band has the disadvantage of being slightly degraded because a 60-Hz wide slot at 2600 Hz is taken for the in-band signaling tone.

Figure 4-7 illustrates in-band and out-of-band signaling frequency relationships. Other frequencies within the 200-3200-Hz voice band also may be used for signaling purposes and may be designated as in-band signaling tones.

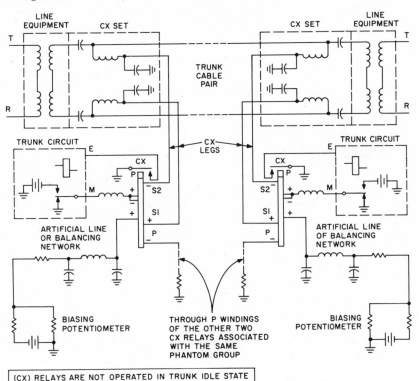

Figure 4-6   Composite (CX) Signaling

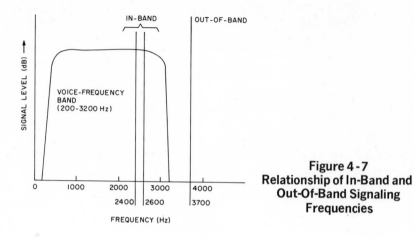

**Figure 4 - 7
Relationship of In-Band and
Out-Of-Band Signaling
Frequencies**

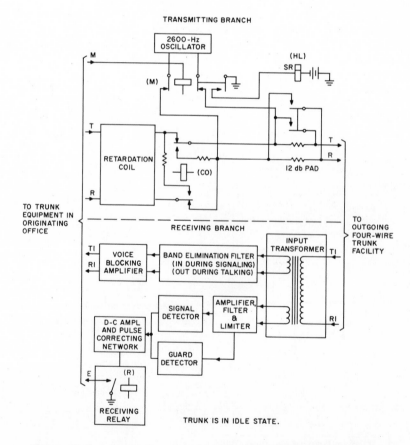

Figure 4-8   Single-Frequency (SF) In-Band Signaling Circuit

Single-Frequency (SF) In-band Signaling System

The 2600-Hz in-band signaling system is one of the standard a-c signaling methods for conveying a variety of information. Figure 4-8 presents the basic components of this particular circuit. Assume that a four-wire trunk providing separate paths for each direction of transmission is idle and equipped for SF in-band signaling; 2600-Hz tone is being transmitted over the trunk in both directions.

When the trunk is seized at its originating terminal, the M lead is changed from the ground to the battery state. Keying relay (M) will operate from the battery on the M lead which will remove the 2600-Hz tone from the outgoing line or trunk pair. The loss of the tone will be detected by the SF signaling unit at the far-end, changing the far-end E lead condition from open to ground, causing the switching equipment to function. (In common-control offices, the connection of an idle incoming register or sender is initiated and in step-by-step offices an incoming selector is connected.) At the same time, the far-end trunk circuit will change its M lead from ground to battery removing the 2600-Hz tone coming from the terminating office to the originating end. Upon receipt of this signal (the absence of 2600 Hz) at the originating office, the E lead changes from the open to the ground condition notifying the switching equipment in the originating office to delay transmission of the address information until an incoming register or selector circuit has been connected to the far-end trunk. When the connection has been made, the distant trunk circuit advances and ground will be restored to its M lead reinstating the 2600-Hz tone to the near-end trunk. With the detection of this tone at the originating trunk terminal, the pulsing of the address information begins.

The (M) relay in the transmitting branch of the SF unit operates and releases in unison with the pulses being transmitted. Thus, it alternately removes and applies the 2600-Hz tone to the outgoing trunk conductors. (M) also initiates the operation of relays (HL) and (CO). The (HL) relay then cuts out the 12 dB pad in the output circuit of the 2600-Hz oscillator in order to increase its power level and thereby improve the signaling reliability. The (HL) relay is a slow-release type designed not to release during the pulsing of the (M) relay. Operation of relay (CO) momentarily opens and terminates the transmission path of the trunk equipment in order to avoid noise or other interference from the central office equipment. A retardation coil is bridged across the trunk transmission path to drain off longitudinal currents that may arise in the central office equipment and interfere with signaling.

The receiving branch of the SF signaling unit includes band-pass and pulse-correction networks, *signal* and *guard detector* circuits, and a voice blocking amplifier. The signal detector operates on the 2600-Hz tone and the guard detector functions on speech frequencies. The outputs of the two detectors oppose each other and provide an additional margin against false operations during speech transmission. The main function of the blocking voice amplifier is to prevent noise or speech present in the switching

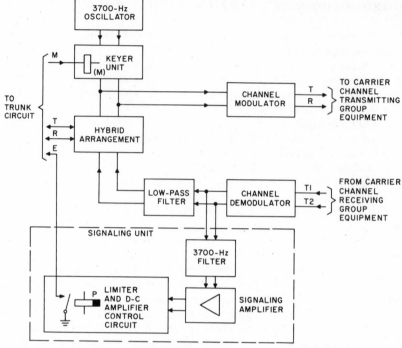

Figure 4-9   3700-Hz Out-Of-Band Signaling Circuit

equipment from interfering with the operation of the signal detector. It also serves to overcome the insertion loss of the SF unit in the receiving speech path. The output of the d-c amplifier includes a pulse correcting circuit which operates the (R) relay to repeat the received signals over the E lead of the trunk equipment.

Out-of-band Signaling Systems

Signaling systems that operate adjacent to the normal voice-frequency band (200-3200 Hz) are designated as out-of-band. The 20-Hz ringing current may be included in this category because this low frequency cannot be transmitted by carrier and voice-frequency equipment. Frequencies just above the 200-3200-Hz band are normally used for out-of-band signaling purposes.

Out-of-band signaling has been incorporated into a number of carrier systems designed for short-haul toll applications. For example, the Bell system types N, O and ON employ 3700 Hz for signaling, and the Lenkurt type 45 carrier uses two tones; 3400 and 3550 Hz for out-of-band signaling. The lack of speech interference and the ability to use higher signal levels, thereby improving signaling reliability, are the main advantages of out-of-band signaling.

Figure 4-9 illustrates the main features of this signaling circuit used with N-type carrier systems. The 3700-Hz tone is transmitted continuously during trunk idle and on-hook conditions. In fact, the signaling operations are very similar to those described for the 2600-Hz in-band signaling arrangement. For instance, when the M lead has battery on it, the 3700-Hz tone is sent through the input of the channel modulator to the distant carrier terminal. At the far-end, after the demodulation process, the 3700-Hz tone is directed through the 3700-Hz filter to the signaling unit. It is blocked from entering the trunk talking path by the low-pass filter which only permits the passage of frequencies in the 200-3200 Hz range. The 3700-Hz tone, after amplification and limiting, is rectified into dc for controlling a polar type relay in the signaling control circuit. This relay is normally held operated by the presence of 3700-Hz tone and opens the E lead. Whenever the tone is removed, this polar relay releases to ground the E lead to indicate receipt of the signal.

In the Lenkurt type 45 carrier equipment, tone frequencies of 3400 and 3550 Hz are used for out-of-band signaling. The 3400-Hz tone is the trunk idle and on-hook indication. Trunk busy and off-hook conditions are conveyed by 3550-Hz tone. Supervision and dial pulsing address signals, impressed on the M lead from the trunk circuit, actuate the signaling oscillator causing it to shift from 3400 to 3550 Hz. The resulting tones are transmitted in the usual manner to the distant trunk terminal for detection and subsequent control of the E lead state. The detailed operations generally follow those for the 3700 Hz-out-of-band signaling unit.

Multifrequency (MF) Signaling

In the previous signaling systems studied, the address information was conveyed by the sequential method of pulsing the digits of the called number. The relays and related equipment associated with the E and M leads of SF signaling handle dial pulses at speeds of approximately 8 to 12 pulses per second. Since each digit requires from 1 to 10 pulses as well as pauses between digits, considerable time is needed for transmitting the called number. While interoffice calls may require only a four-digit transmission, tandem and short-haul toll calls send seven digits and inter-toll calls may require ten digits if calling out of the local area code. The multifrequency (MF) pulsing method, developed by the Bell System for rapidly transmitting address information between central offices, uses a-c signals in the voice-frequency range. It transmits the digits by combinations of only 2 of 5 frequencies; supplementary signals are furnished by using a sixth frequency in combinations with one of the others.

Multifrequency tone pulsing requires the same amount of time for one complete digit as it takes to dial one pulse. Thus a ten-digit number can be sent by MF in about the same time as it takes to transmit the 0 digit by dial pulsing. The advantages of MF signaling are best employed where collected and stored address information, as in common-control offices, must be transmitted to another storage or translation point or where the terminating central office can utilize the MF signals without further conversion.

MF pulsing only transmits address information; other signaling methods, such as CX, DX, or SX, are still required for trunk control and status supervision functions.

Figure 4-10 lists the six frequencies comprising multifrequency codes. These frequencies are 200 Hz apart in the 700-1700 Hz range. Two frequencies are sent simultaneously for each digit or supplementary signal. Fifteen combinations are possible with 10 in use for the digits 0 to 9 and the symbols KP for request for key pulsing sender and ST indicating the completion of keying and the start of circuit operations. The remaining three combinations are reserved for future requirements.

Multifrequency (MF) Signaling Code

Digit	Frequencies (Hz)	Digit	Frequencies (Hz)
1	700 + 900	7	700 + 1500
2	700 + 1100	8	900 + 1500
3	900 + 1100	9	1100 + 1500
4	700 + 1300	0	1300 + 1500
5	900 + 1300	KP	1100 + 1700
6	1100 + 1300	ST	1500 + 1700

KP = Signal to start MF pulsing.
ST = Signal to indicate end of MF pulsing.

Figure 4-10

MF pulsing is initiated either by manual keysets on toll or DSA switchboards or by MF outpulsing senders in common-control offices such as the crossbar type. In the terminating central office, a MF receiver is connected to the incoming sender or register link circuit. Because MF pulsing is very rapid and only occurs during the period when a connection is being established, a relatively small number of senders or registers equipped with MF receivers need to be provided as common equipment for a large number of trunks.

The principal elements of MF signaling for a toll switchboard trunk connected to a crossbar central office are shown in Fig. 4-11. The operator, after selecting an idle trunk, presses the KP button on the keyset to signal the distant sender or register link equipment to connect to a MF receiver. The S lamp on the keyset will light when the far-end equipment is ready to receive the MF pulses. After keypulsing the digits of the called number, the operator presses the ST button, indicating the end of pulsing and also disconnecting the keyset from the operator's cord circuit and extinguishing the KP and S lamps. If the operator inadvertently presses two buttons simultaneously, the MF receiver at the distant office will detect the variation from the standard code pattern and send a reorder signal. The operator then releases the connection and initiates the call again.

At the terminating central office, the two MF tones of each digit are amplified and limited in the MF receiver unit associated with the incoming sender and register circuit. The frequencies are selected by appropriate channel filters in the MF receiver and then detected; the resultant d-c

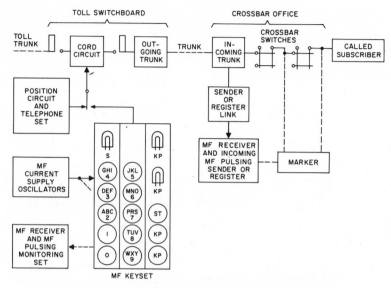

**Figure 4 - 11   Multifrequency (MF) Pulsing From Toll
Switchboard to Crossbar Central Office**

voltage will cause the operation of the proper channel relays. The specific digit sent is denoted by the particular channel relays placing ground on 2 of the 5 leads to the sender register circuit. At the end of each MF signal, the circuit will advance, waiting for receipt of the next digit. Once the ST signal is sent (1500 + 1700 Hz) at the end of the last digit, the MF receiver will disconnect from the incoming sender and register-link circuits.

Review Questions

1. What are the two main categories and usages of interoffice signaling?
2. Name four d-c loop signaling methods. Which one is used in present electromechanical switching systems and for what primary purpose?
3. What is the idle trunk polarity condition? What is the trunk polarity when the called party answers?
4. What method may be used when the trunk conductor resistance between offices is too high for satisfactory loop pulsing?
5. What is the principal trunk signaling scheme? What are its functions?
6. What are the near-end E and M lead conditions of a trunk equipped with DX signaling when the called party has not answered?
7. What are the main types of a-c signaling systems that are used on trunks? What frequencies do they employ?
8. What are the basic components in the receiving branch of the SF in-band signaling unit?
9. What are the E and M lead conditions on an idle trunk equipped for out-of-band signaling? Why?
10. How many frequencies comprise the multifrequency (MF) code? What is its speed of transmission as compared to dial pulsing?

5

Switching Network Fundamentals

Central Office Functions

The local central office performs two important functions; namely, interconnecting and control. Interconnection may be defined as the function that provides individual talking paths between all subscribers served by a particular office, in addition to completing talking paths through other central offices and switching centers. The interconnecting capability does not necessarily mean simultaneous connections of all or even most subscriber lines. If, for instance, all subscribers in a central office desire to talk to each other at the same time, the number of connections required within the office would have to be equal to one-half the number of subscribers. Fortunately, only a small portion of subscribers, normally about 10 to 14 percent, originate calls at a given time, requiring that the switching network have a capacity for simultaneously handling only that percent of the number of subscribers using a particular office. A central office serving 4000 subscriber lines would probably not have more than about 500 calls in progress simultaneously, requiring that the equipment be able to provide only that many simultaneous connections.

The control function is the most complex of the central office activities for it controls the interconnecting operations and associated equipment. In step-by-step systems, the control function consists primarily of relays controlling the operations of the various selector switches. In common-control systems, the register sender, decoder, and marker circuits usually provide the principal control functions.

Need for Centralized Switching

The prime function of a central office is to establish a communication path between any two telephones it serves or between a telephone and another central office. Figure 5-1 illustrates a microtelephone system of

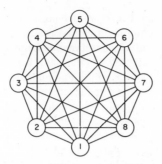

Figure 5-1   Elementary Telephone System with Direct Interconnections

eight directly connected subscribers. A series of paths are provided between all stations. In order that each subscriber may talk to any of the other
seven, a total of 28 paths would be needed in addition to seven switches
at each telephone, permitting each subscriber to select any of the other
stations. Only four calls can be made when half of the subscribers talks
to the other half. Obviously the direct connection method is impractical
as well as uneconomical.

Centralized switching is the most practical and economical because
subscribers are not directly connected. Instead, each telephone is connected
to a central office by a pair of wires. The switching equipment in the office
establishes the connections on command of each telephone. See Fig. 5-2.

Switching Network Principles

In theory, most switching systems should have *full access* capabilities and should be *nonblocking*. Full access means that every subscriber
can be connected to every other subscriber, although not necessarily at
the same time. Nonblocking means than an originating subscriber usually
can be connected to any other idle subscriber, irrespective of the number
of existing connections.

Refer again to Fig. 5-2 and note that 4 interconnections would be needed to handle the maximum number of simultaneous connections. However,
the number of times when all 4 connections are required is rare, in fact

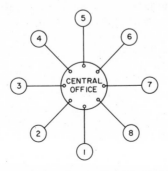

Figure 5-2   Centralized Switching

it is doubtful if more than 2 links would normally be necessary. Therefore considerable savings in equipment can be realized by designing the switching network to provide only 2 simultaneous connections. Figure 5-3 illustrates an elementary switching network for 8 subscribers that conforms to the requirements of full access and nonblocking principles. Two switches are provided at the originating appearance of the subscriber lines for concentrating the 8 lines to 2 links. Two switches are also used at the terminating positions of the lines to connect either link to the desired subscriber line. Switches 1 and 2 are joined together to form part of *linefinder* circuit 1, and switches 4 and 5 form part of linefinder 2. Telephone 2 (the calling subscriber) in the figure will be connected by switches 1 and 2 to link 1 which terminates in switch 3. The called line 6 will be selected by switch 3. Similarly, calling subscriber 7 will be connected through link 2 to called line 3. Note that both links are accessible to linefinder circuits 1 and 2.

The interconnection of the concentration and expansion switches or stages in the figure may be termed the distribution method as applied to switching systems. These stages of concentration, distribution and expansion form the basis of switching systems such as step-by-step, panel and crossbar to be studied in detail later.

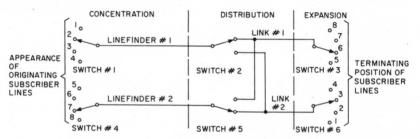

Figure 5-3   Elementary Switching Network

Direct-Control Switching Criteria

Step-by-step switching is a form of the direct control and progressive method of processing address information. In this system the various selecting switches of the interconnecting network are under the direct control of the dial pulses transmitted by the subscriber. The registration of this information, sent in the form of dial pulses or tones, is performed by the selecting or interconnecting switches. Thus there is a fixed relationship between the speed of the dial pulse and the stepping speed or motion of the selecting switches. The system must be designed to handle the number of pulses for each dialed digit, ranging from 1 to 10.

The mechanical switches normally used in step-by-step, direct, progressive control switching are of the double action kind. They are composed of both a selection and hunting stage except that the last switch has 2 selection stages. These selecting switches are designed to step a maximum of 10 levels vertically in unison with the dial pulses. In the hunting stage, the switch normally rotates horizontally over 10 terminals in searching for an idle path. The restriction on the number of hunting outlets is a requirement of the time interval between the digits dialed by the calling subscriber.

One disadvantage of the direct-control switching network is that the called number specifically locates the called line on the last switching stage, called the *connector*. Figure 5-4 illustrates the 10 levels in the banks of a connector switch and the corresponding assignments of the tens and units digits of the called line number. For example, assume that 1652 is the called number. The last 2 numbers, 52, will be on the fifth level and the second horizontal point. Number 2117 would have the tens digit on the first level and the units digit on the seventh horizontal point. However, line numbers with 0 as the tens digit always will be on the tenth level. A traffic overload would therefore exist if numerous subscribers receiving many calls should be assigned line numbers in the same hundreds group. For instance numbers in the series 0900-0999 would be served by the same connector switch or 2100-2199 would appear on the same connector.

A condition of traffic overload can also occur on trunk groups that connect to other central offices. The office code assignments define the exact levels to which the switches are stepped. Office code 234, for instance, requires that the first selector step to the second level, the second selector to the third level, and the third selector to the fourth level. It is not possible to vary this routing in order to avoid an overload condition between central offices.

One further disadvantage to this system is the fixed association between assigned central office codes and trunk location on the switches. Once the subscriber has dialed the 3 digits of the office code, it is impossible to direct the switches to an alternate trunk route. Thus, if all trunks are busy or a trouble condition is encountered along the selected path in the network, the subscriber will just receive a busy signal as an indication to disconnect and dial again.

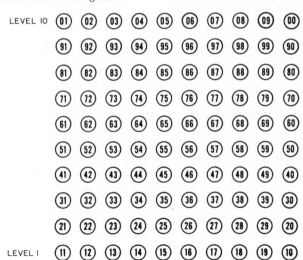

Figure 5-4   Schematic of Wiring of Terminals on Connector Switch

Direct-Control Switching Functions

Elementary, direct control, progressive switching, as shown in Fig. 5-5, is composed of three selection stages which require that a four-digit number be dialed. The third stage, controlled by the tens and units digits, is of the double selection type using a connector switch. The off-hook signal from the calling subscriber's line actuates the linefinder circuit which connects the calling line terminals to the associated 1st selection stage. Dial tone is sent to the calling subscriber by the first selector circuit and the subscriber begins to dial the four digits of the called number which might be 3401. The dial pulses for the first or thousands digit (#3) will induce the selection control circuit of the first selection stage to step the switch vertically to the third level. When the control circuit recognizes the end of the dialed digit, it will actuate the self-operating hunting stage associated with the first selector. This hunting stage, through rotary motion in the horizontal plane, will search for and connect an idle outlet to the next selection stage.

Similarly the second selector will be directed by the pulses of the hundreds digit (#4) to its fourth level. The second selector's hunting stage will automatically seek an idle path to the last stage which is the connector switch. The dial pulses for the tens digit (#0) will cause the control circuit of this last stage to advance the connector switch to its tenth vertical level. Since this stage is not designed for hunting, the pulses for the units digit (#1) will step the connector switch horizontally one position. The last stage now is connected to the called line #3401. The line busy-test circuit of the connector switch proceeds to test the called line. It cuts through the transmission path and applies ringing current if the line is idle. If it is busy, a busy-tone signal will be sent back to the calling subscriber.

Features of Common-Control System

Generally direct, progressive control switching as in the step-by-step system is efficient and economical for small size telephone networks. The control functions are simple as well as easy to understand and maintain. However, the various disadvantages preclude efficient operation for multi-office installations. These factors, coupled with the rapid rise in the number and scope of telephone service, hastened the development of common-control switching systems.

The two main features of an electromechanical common-control system are the use of large capacity switches and the use of circuits provided for temporary storing and translating the dial pulses into appropriate control signals to guide the switch network. In the panel dial system, for example, switches such as district and office frames have access to 500 levels. A series of crossbar switches in the crossbar system can furnish access to several thousand outlets. In contrast, step-by-step selecting switches have a capacity of 10 levels with 10 paths on each level, or a possible total of 100 outlets.

In a common-control system the equipment provided for receiving and storing dial pulses and controlling the switching functions is termed the register sender. It is selected by a link circuit. The linefinder operates under

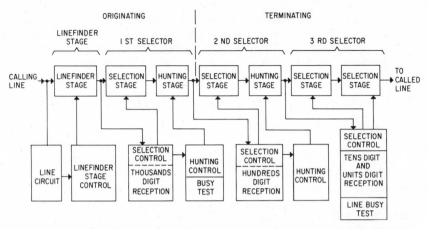

Figure 5-5 Elementary Direct-Control and Progressive Switching System

common control when a subscriber initiates a call by going off-hook. Therefore it is independent of any information dialed by the subscriber. A very short interval is required for the linefinder to reach the calling subscriber's line terminals and to connect a link to an idle register sender circuit. A tone signal informs the calling subscriber when the register sender is ready to receive his instructions.

Functions of Register-Sender in the Common-Control Progressive System

The register-sender in a common-control switching system, progressive type, such as a panel dial office, normally performs the following three basic functions:

1. It receives and temporarily stores the dial pulses received which represent the digits of the called number.

2. It translates these pulses into appropriate control signals. The first three digits, representing the office code, may need the generation of corresponding routing selection signals.

3. It maintains control of selections by the switching apparatus in the central offices.

For a local area call, the first three digits are the calling subscriber's office code; the last four digits are the called line number. In order to speed up operations, two separate translation methods are used. As soon as the first three digits are registered, the office-code translation circuit is activated. The resulting control information directing the selection of a trunk to the terminating central office equipment will be temporarily stored in the register-sender. These operations are performed while other digits are being registered.

As soon as the trunk to the terminating panel office is seized, the register-sender then controls the selections of the called line number. This control is a function of the information registered within the line number translation unit. The translation process depends upon a fixed relationship between the line number and the control signal code. The register-sender exercises this direction by counting the revertive pulses sent back from the incoming and final selection stages, as will be described.

Elementary Common-Control Progressive System

Figure 5-6 illustrates a simplified panel dial system, a progressive type of common-control system whose operations are governed by the register-sender.

As in direct-control switching, the off-hook signal from a subscriber causes a linefinder to connect to the terminals of the calling line. The link circuit associated with the linefinder will signal the sender link connector to search for an idle register-sender which will send back a dial tone to the calling subscriber.

Once the register-sender has recorded the first three dialed digits (the office code), it will call in the office code translation circuit called the de-

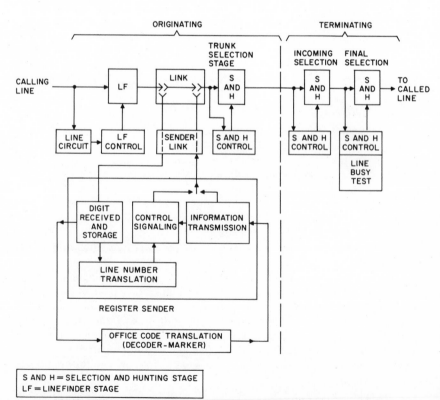

Figure 5-6   Elementary Common-Control Switching System, Progressive Control

coder marker. The decoder marker translates the office code into information for controlling the selection of a trunk group to the terminating office and then is immediately disconnected once translation is complete. The register-sender then continues with its control of the trunk selection stage while the four digits of the line number are being registered.

As soon as a trunk is selected and a connection established with the terminating office, the register-sender will advance to control the selection stages in the terminating equipment. In the meantime, the line number translation unit of the register-sender converts the four dialed digits into corresponding selection control signals which will govern the incoming and final selection stages of the terminating equipment until the connection has been completed with the terminals of the called line.

The four digits of the called line have a range of 10,000 numbers, 0000 through 9999. These numbers are divided into twenty groups of 500 each for the incoming selection stage. The particular group selected is determined by the thousands and hundreds digits that were dialed. Therefore line number 2345 would be in the fifth group; number 6789 would be in the fourteenth group.

The tens and units digits of the dialed number direct the final stage to the correct number. The register-sender is released as soon as the final selections are completed and the link circuit, associated with the linefinder, will then connect the calling subscriber to the already selected and waiting trunk. The path between the calling and called lines is now complete. The final selector must test the called line. If it is idle, ringing current will be applied and if busy the final circuit will send back a busy tone signal.

Grid Network Common-Control System

The establishment of a call through a progressive network is relatively slow. The full use of alternate routings and possible second trial features by the register sender, therefore, is usually not practical. In fact it is usually necessary for calls between offices to transmit the switching control signals rather than just the number information. This sort of interoffice signaling is necessarily limited in speed and range restricting the full use of the register-sender in common-control systems. Most of these disadvantages, however, have been overcome in grid switching and marker type common-control systems, illustrated here by the crossbar dial system.

The *crossbar switch, marker,* and *originating* and *terminating registers* are the basic elements of the grid network or crossbar common-control system. The crossbar switch is composed of 20 vertical and 10 horizontal contact elements mounted on a common frame. Each vertical element is actually a 10-point switch. Connections from a common terminal to any one of 10 individual terminals is accomplished by selectively operated sets of relay-type contacts. The individual terminals of all vertical units can be multiplied horizontally so that each input on the vertical side can be connected to any of the 10 outputs on the horizontal side. Note in Fig. 5-7, a typical crossbar switch, that the crosspoints of vertical #9 and horizontal #3, vertical #17 and horizontal #1, and vertical #15 and horizontal #8 are connected.

In the direct- and common-control progressive systems, each selection stage, except the last one, hunts for an idle trunk or path automatically. However, because it is not practical to provide automatic hunting over adjacent terminals in a crossbar switch, the trunk and path busy-test functions are performed by the marker circuit. This method permits individual trunks or a group to be dispersed over various parts of the grid network or crossbar switch frames. Since successive tests of individual trunks would take considerable time, the test leads from trunks in the desired group are tested simultaneously by the marker. The marker controls the switching network in accordance with the information received from the office code translator and the originating register.

The originating register records the dialed digits. Once the first 3 digits have been received, this register connects to a marker which is directed to set up a path or connection between the calling line location on the switch frame and the trunk to the called terminating office. The terminating register then handles the completion of incoming calls. It connects to the incoming trunks and records the called line number transmitted from the originating register located in the calling office. The terminating register will then call in a marker to establish a connection through the grid network to the switch location of the called line.

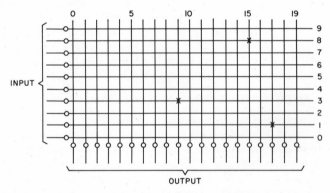

Figure 5-7   Elements of a Crossbar Switch

Elementary Crossbar Common-Control System

The common-control functions in a grid switching and marker system are considerably greater than in the progressive type. Figure 5-8 illustrates an elementary crossbar system. The control functions are directed by the originating and terminating registers and the marker unit.

As a call is begun, the off-hook line condition operates the subscriber's line relay in the *line relay frame*. This frame serves all subscriber lines for both originating and terminating calls. The subscriber's line relay circuit causes the connector to select an idle originating register which sends a dial tone back to the calling subscriber. As soon as the first 3 digits are recorded by the originating register, it will call immediately for a marker in order to transmit the location of the calling line and the office code information.

The marker translates the office code information and locates an idle trunk to the terminating central office. Next, the marker informs the originating register that the called line number should be pulsed out to the terminating office equipment; it then releases. Less than 0.5 seconds is the average holding time for the marker to complete these functions.

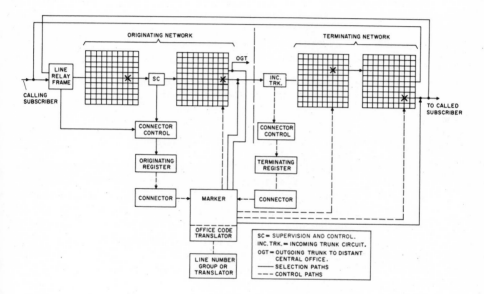

Figure 5-8   Elementary Crossbar Common-Control Switching System

In the same local office, the incoming trunk will be connected by the *connector control* circuit to an idle terminating register, causing the originating register to outpulse the called line number, usually in the form of MF pulses. The terminating register, after connecting to a marker, will transmit the line number and the switch location of the incoming trunk. Note that this marker is the same one serving the originating central office.

The marker utilizes a line number group or translator circuit to determine the switch location of the called number. If the line tests idle, the marker will establish a connection between the incoming trunk and the switch location of the called line. If the line tests busy, the marker will connect the incoming trunk to a busy-tone signal. Supervisory and control circuits, associated with the originating network and the incoming trunk equipment in the terminating network, take over the supervisory functions of a call as soon as the originating and terminating registers and the marker release.

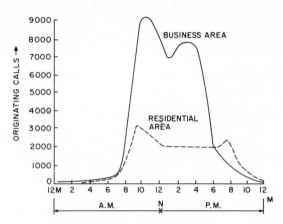

Figure 5-9   Typical Weekday, Hourly Traffic Loads in Business and Residential Central Offices

Telephone Traffic Characteristics

Characteristics of telephone traffic necessarily influence the design and capacity of switching systems. The number of simultaneously originated calls, for example, can affect the amount and type of common control equipment, such as registers and markers, that will be necessary. Or the duration of holding time of calls during busy hours will determine the number of switching paths and the capacity of the central office. It is essential, of course, for good service that adequate switching paths and trunks be provided, but in the interest of economy the number of paths and trunks should be kept small.

Daily variations in telephone traffic loads are extremely pronounced; there is a marked difference in the hourly and daily distribution of traffic loads between business and residential subscribers. These deviations, shown in Fig. 5-9, illustrate a typical weekday traffic load for central offices serving business and residential areas. The telephone traffic serving business rises rapidly starting about 7:30 A.M. and reaches a peak between 10:00 A.M. and 11:00 A.M., receding about 25 percent during the middle of the day. A smaller peak occurs in the afternoon between 2:00 P.M. and 4:30 P.M. dropping off rapidly after those times and decreasing to about 5 percent of its peak load by 8:00 P.M. The residential traffic, however, has its peak between 9:00 and 10:00 A.M. and then stays fairly constant until the evening hours when it peaks between 7:00 and 8:00 P.M. Both business and residential traffic is at a minimum during the night.

Traffic Engineering Rudiments

Telephone traffic may be defined as the total time taken by circuits, switches, trunks or other paths to handle calls. The amount of traffic may be calculated for any period as the product of the number of calls during the period and the average holding time per call. It may also be computed

Telephone Traffic Units

U C = Unit call (expressed in 100 seconds or CCS)
CCS = Hundred-second calls or the total amount of traffic in seconds divided by 100.
ERLANG = Traffic unit used when holding times are expressed in hours. It usually is designated as E.
E = 36 CCS and CCS = E/36

Figure 5-10

as the product of the average number of occupied circuits or trunks during a period and the duration of the period in time units. For instance, a trunk during the busy hour may handle 12 calls, each of 3 minutes average duration. Since the calls must be carried in sequence by the trunk, the total time in use will be 36 minutes or 0.6 hours. The busy-hour trunk occupancy, therefore, will be 60%.

It follows that telephone traffic may be expressed in any convenient time unit because it is equivalent to the length of occupancy of the switching channel. This occupancy may consist of a few calls of long holding times, many calls of short duration, or any combination of these calls as long as the aggregate of the individual holding time is equal to the total length of occupancy. Accordingly, traffic can be expressed in units of hours, minutes or seconds depending upon which particular unit is used for the holding time.

Traffic density is the traffic per unit of time. It is expressed either in CCS or in Erlangs and the time normally is in hours. The commonly used traffic units and their correlations are shown in Fig. 5-10. The applications of these traffic units may be illustrated by the following examples: (a) For 20 calls, each of 150 seconds average duration, the equivalent unit call will be 30 CCS (20 × 150/100); (b) 18 calls, each of 200 seconds duration, will comprise a traffic of 36 CCS or a traffic density equal to 1 Erlang per hour (18 × 200/3600).

Traffic Load Factors

The actual number of calls originated hourly through the day, especially during busy-hour periods, is a useful measure of telephone traffic loads. The number of calls originated per hour multiplied by the average holding time in 100 seconds equals the CCS load factor. The average holding time will become relatively constant for a large number of calls. The traffic load factor determines the number of simultaneous calls that may be expected during busy-hour periods in a particular switching channel or trunk group. The following general equation may be utilized for this purpose:

$$C_{ns} = \frac{nh}{3600}$$

where C_{ns} = average number of simultaneous calls during specific hourly period.

n = number of calls originated during specific hourly period.

h = average holding time in seconds.

If 180 calls are originated during the busy hour in central office A destined for office B, assuming an average holding time of 100 seconds, we will obtain the following using the above equation:

$$C_{ns} = \frac{nh}{3600} = \frac{180 \times 100}{3600} = 5 \text{ simultaneous calls.}$$

If these 180 calls were placed end to end, they would extend over a five-hour period or would be five rows of 36 calls each, in 1 hour. Moreover, if these same 180 calls had an average holding time of 200 seconds, the number of simultaneous calls would be 10, using the equation. Traffic load fluctuations generally follow the theory of probability. The hourly variations for any one day are likely to occur on other days.

Grade of Service Probability

An important factor in traffic engineering is the grade of service that must be provided by the switching system. Because only a small percentage of subscribers originate calls at any given instant, the number of switching channels and trunks needed to carry the amount of simultaneous calls is only a fraction of the number of subscriber lines connected to the central office. According to the theory of probability, if a low number of switching channels and trunks is installed, there is no assurance that service demands can be met satisfactorily at all times. It can therefore be anticipated that a small percentage of calls will be blocked during peak traffic periods. When this occurs an overflow, or an all-trunk busy, signal will be returned to the subscriber, indicating that it is necessary for the number to be redialed.

The number of uncompleted or blocked calls due to busy paths or trunks in the busy hour is an index of the grade of service rendered by a switching system. The grade of service can therefore be related to the probability that a certain percentage of calls originated during the busy hour will not be completed and must be repeated. The grade of service is expressed by the P factor. P.01 means that there is a probability that 1 call in 100 will be uncompleted; P.05 indicates that five calls in one hundred will be blocked, etc. Generally it is desirable that switching systems be engineered to provide at least P.04 grade of service during the busy periods. On the average, traffic in the busy hour is about 10 percent of the total 24-hour traffic. Therefore the number of switching channels or trunks that are furnished for a busy hour P.04 grade of service will afford a much higher quality of service during the other periods of the day.

Traffic studies indicate that about 15 to 20 percent of attempted calls are not completed during the busy hour because of busy or no-answer conditions. However, there are ample justifications for furnishing a high grade of service in central offices. First, repeated and ineffective attempts reduce the efficiency of switching equipment and interoffice trunks by unnecessarily holding them busy. Furthermore, the grade of service can deteriorate considerably even by a moderate increase in traffic when busy conditions are encountered. Moreover, the subscriber may become apprehen-

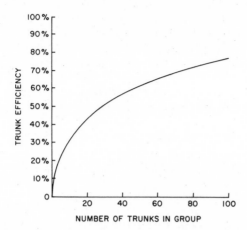

Figure 5-11   Trunk Efficiency Relationships

sive of receiving busy signals on repeated call attempts when he may have reason to assume that the called line is idle. As a result, it is desirable to specify a good grade of service for normally busy periods in order to avoid possible critical impairment of service during unusual and unexpected traffic peaks. Traffic data and the prescribed grade of service help to determine the number of switching channels and trunks needed in the design of a central office.

Switching Paths and Trunk Group Efficiencies

Large groups of switching channels or trunks are generally more efficient in handling heavy traffic than smaller groups since traffic has a better chance to level out and the peaks tend to be lower than in smaller systems. The probability of this occuring is apparent when a large group of 40 trunks is divided into 4 subgroups of 10. During traffic peaks, all 10 trunks in the first subgroup may be busy, although there may be idle paths in the other subgroups. However, if all 40 trunks were in a single group, no calls would be blocked until all the trunks were in use.

The relationship between the size of a trunk group and its efficiency of operation is not linear. Figure 5-11 shows that as the size of a trunk group increases, the efficiency rises rapidly at first and then tends to level off. If the number of trunks in the previous example were doubled to 20, the efficiency increases by 50 percent. But doubling the number of trunks from 20 to 40 yields an increase of only 30 percent. The result will be the same if a trunk group of 40 is enlarged to 80 trunks. There is only an efficiency advance of about 20 percent, and an increase from 80 to 100 trunks results in an advance of only about 4 percent.

Review Questions

1. What two important switching functions are performed by the central office? Which one is most complex and why?

2. What is the basic concept of centralized switching? What two features are essential to switching networks? Define.

3. Define step-by-step switching. What are some disadvantages?

4. What are the two main features of electromechanical common-control switching?

5. What three basic functions are performed by the register-sender?

6. What are the disadvantages of the common-control progressive switching system?

7. What common-control system overcomes the disadvantages of the progressive type? What are its basic elements?

8. What information is received by the marker? What are its main functions?

9. In what units is telephone traffic normally expressed? Define them.

10. What is the general formula for determining the number of simultaneous calls that may be expected during busy-hour periods?

6

Central Office Power

Power Supply Sources

Central offices and switching centers furnish various forms of electric power for talking, signaling, ringing and supervisory functions in the telephone system. Equipment is provided for the production, regulation, distribution and protection of the generated electrical energy and additional apparatus and circuits are provided to transmit any alarms of trouble conditions in the power supply units and facilities. Central office power plants must be designed for utmost reliability at all times because they are the primary power source for the telephone system.

The main sources of power in a central office are storage batteries, d-c generators, a-c generators, including ringing machines, tone generators, and interrupting equipment. A powerboard is used to control, regulate, distribute, and protect the different power supply sources.

The electric power commonly required in a modern central office includes the following main categories:

48 volts dc. 48 volts dc (nominally) is used for voice transmission and for operation of the switching and control equipment.

24 volts dc. In certain offices 24 volts dc is used for specific carrier and microwave radio terminals. This voltage is used for common-battery operation with manual switchboards.

130 volts dc. 130 volts dc are used to furnish the plate voltage for amplifiers, carrier terminals and other equipment containing vacuum tubes. This power rating is also used for cable carrier systems of the pulse code modulation (PCM) type to power a series of regenerative repeaters along a cable pair.

75-150 volts ac. 75-150 volts ac at 20 Hz, or at various frequencies in the range of 16 to 67 Hz (harmonic ringing), is used to supply ringing current for subscriber signaling.

Various a-c tones. Various a-c tones (both steady and interrupted) and d-c pulses are used to provide audible and sometimes visual indications of different conditions of the equipment and circuits in the central office.

Emergency Power Equipment

Central offices normally operate from commercial a-c power mains. Solid-state rectifiers or rotary converters (motor-generator sets) convert this a-c power to 48 - 50 volts dc. This is the primary voltage for operating the central office equipment and keeping the storage batteries fully charged. Figure 6 - 1 illustrates the essential elements of a central office power plant.

The ringing generator, tone generator, and the various interrupters usually are combined on a single motor unit for operation from the commercial a-c power or from the 48-volt battery. These units usually are installed in pairs to ensure service continuity and two or more d-c charging units are also provided to safeguard service in case one should fail.

In the event of a commercial power failure, the central office 48-volt storage battery becomes the sole primary power source. It maintains service during any failure of the d-c generators, charging units or failure during transfer operations between d-c generator units. Emergency power units such as an engine-driven generator are installed in almost all central offices. This auxiliary power plant is generally composed of a gas turbine, gasoline or diesel engine which drives an a-c generator. It is designed to start automatically in case of a commercial power failure, especially in the smaller central offices. One or more of these emergency units may be installed depending upon the size of the central office and the busy-hour load requirements. However, the emergency power plant should have sufficient capacity to supply the maximum busy-hour load plus any other needed emergency equipment.

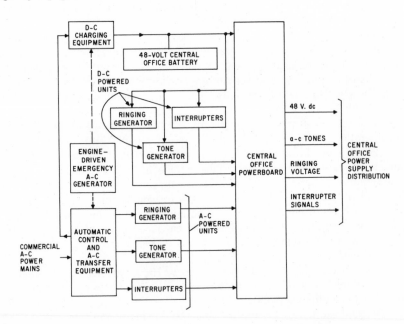

Figure 6 - 1   **Central Office Power Supply Equipment**

Central Office Battery

The 48-volt central office battery serves three chief purposes:

1. It acts as a filter across the d-c generator or rectifier output to smooth out the resultant d-c supply.

2. It provides additional power that may be needed for peak loads.

3. In the event of an a-c power or d-c generator failure, it can continue to supply emergency power to the central office equipment.

The capacity of the central office battery and the kind of associated control equipment depend upon the size and type of central office equipment, reliability of the commercial a-c power and the presence of engine-driven emergency power generating units. In general, assuming that an engine-driven emergency unit is provided, the battery should have sufficient capacity to supply the average busy-hour load continuously for a period of about three to five hours in case of a power failure.

A group of lead-acid electric storage cells, connected in series or in series-parallel, comprise the central office battery. The electric cell is a chemical device which stores electrical energy in the form of potential chemical energy. It consists of a container, usually glass, and electrode plates immersed in an electrolyte which stores the chemical energy. When the cell is fully charged, the stored energy within the electrolyte will create a potential difference of about 2.05 to 2.15 volts between the cell's terminals. When the battery is supplying power, the cell loses potential energy and the voltage gradually decreases. However, the voltage should not be permitted to fall below about 1.75 volts for the reserve power of the cell will be exhausted. Any further discharge will cause the voltage to rapidly drop to zero. A completely discharged cell usually causes permanent damage to the electrode plates.

In the smaller central offices, serving less than 1000 subscriber lines, the central office battery is normally composed of 23 cells connected in series. This arrangement provides a battery voltage of 47 - 49 volts. In larger central offices, a 23-cell battery with three additional "end cells" commonly is installed, as shown in Fig. 6 - 2. In the event of an a-c power failure, the 23 regular cells immediately will furnish the central office power. If the potential of these cells drops below some preset value, such as 46.5 volts, the three end-cells will automatically be connected in series with the 23 cells creating a 26-cell battery with a possible potential of around 52 volts.

Another kind of central office battery contains 24 cells in series with one counterelectromotive force (CEMF) cell, see Fig. 6 - 3. This type is often provided in central offices serving about 1,200 subscriber lines or less. The CEMF cell is a special battery that can develop a potential equal to but opposing that of a regular cell. One type employs a sodium hydroxide (alkaline) electrolyte and nickel or stainless-steel electrodes. The CEMF developed by this cell is in the range of 1.70 to 2.25 volts, depending upon the central office load current; the greater the load current, the higher the CEMF. A dry CEMF cell made of special plates is also available but in current capacities ranging from one to several thousand amperes.

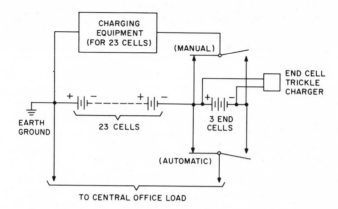

Figure 6-2   Central Office Battery with End Cells

When a commercial power failure occurs, the 24 cells in series with the CEMF cell continue to carry the central office load. If the resultant battery potential (24 cells plus one CEMF cell) should fall to a preset value between 46 and 47 volts, the CEMF cell will be shorted-out automatically, increasing the battery potential to approximately 49 volts.

The life of the central office battery depends upon its proper maintenance, which includes the charging and discharging cycles. The condition of a battery usually is indicated by changes in the composition of the plates, the specific gravity of the electrolyte, and the voltage of the individual cells. The battery must be protected from excessive heat and, therefore, should not be located near steam pipes, radiators, boilers and other heat generating equipment, should be shielded from the direct rays of the sun, and always have some ventilation. A warm battery tends to self-discharge at an accelerated rate which may shorten its life.

An equalizing charge often is given to the central office battery at regular intervals or whenever one or more individual cells have a lower potential than the other cells. The equalizing charge is produced by raising the rectifier or d-c generator output voltage to approximately 2.30 volts per cell; the exact value will depend upon the type of cells and the load requirements of the battery.

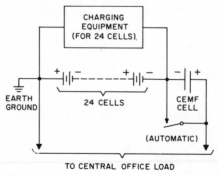

Figure 6-3   Central Office Battery with CEMF Cell

D-C Generating Equipment

D-C generating units, consisting of motor-generator sets or dry-disc rectifiers, normally are connected in parallel with the central office battery. These generators furnish the d-c power for the operation of the central office equipment and charge the battery. Normally d-c generators produce a constant potential that is slightly greater than the battery voltage, sending a small current through the battery in a direction opposite to the discharging current flow. The battery "floats" across the line in this method, keeping the battery fully charged at all times. This is commonly known as "float-charging."

Motor-generator sets usually are found in the larger and older central offices. They are composed of a d-c generator driven by an a-c motor connected to the commercial power lines. A d-c generator of the compound-wound, diverter-pole type often is used and will generate a constant voltage from no-load to about 100 percent of the unit's rated capacity. If the load current from the d-c generator should exceed this value, the diverter-pole windings will cause the output voltage to decrease, thereby preventing an overload condition. An excessive load can cause the voltage of the d-c generator to fall below that of the central office battery. In this event, the battery will deliver power to the load in parallel with the generator. If the d-c generator voltage should fall below the battery voltage due to a failure condition, a reverse current will start to flow from the battery back to the generator. To prevent this, a reverse-current relay on the powerboard will open the generator circuit. Any further back-flow of current from the battery, which might induce the generator to operate as a motor, will be prevented.

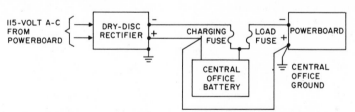

Figure 6-4   Simplified Rectifier Charging Circuit

Solid-state, rectifier charger units, operating from the a-c commercial power, normally provide the 48-volt d-c supply in the average central office in addition to charging the central office battery. The d-c output is filtered first and then sent to the battery and the central office load. These rectifiers produce a constant voltage from no-load to maximum output and if the load should exceed the maximum capacity of the rectifier unit, an over-load protection circuit will function. The central office battery, in this case, also will furnish the additional current needed. The solid-state rectifier has inherent high resistance to reverse current flow or to reverse potential from the battery. Reverse-current relays, therefore, are not required and if a rectifier or a-c power failure should occur, a relay in the powerboard will disconnect the rectifier from the battery circuit. See Fig. 6-4.

When end cells are provided with a 23-cell central office battery, a small rectifier unit or trickle-charger is provided. This unit maintains a potential of about 6.45 volts to float-charge the end cells as shown in Fig. 6-2. The trickle-charger has a small capacity which is not adequate for charging the end cells. Therefore, in the event of a power failure or other discharge, the end cells will be recharged by the regular charging equipment in series with the regular 23 cells.

The central office battery normally is kept fully charged by the d-c generators or rectifier units. These charging units generally maintain the battery potential at 2.15 volts per cell or 0.10 volts above the full charge value of 2.05 volts per cell. In this manner, the cells are sustained at full charge once they have attained that state. The float-charge potential for a 23-cell battery is about 49.5 volts and approximately 51.6 volts for a 24-cell battery.

Normally the positive terminal of the central office battery is grounded as shown in Fig. 6-4. The leads from the positive terminals of the d-c generator and charging equipment are also grounded, requiring fuses only in the negative leads of the central office battery supply. To ensure a good low-resistance ground, connection often is made to buried copper plates and to the steel structure of the building. The main distributing frame (MDF) and the powerboard usually are connected directly to the central office battery ground. In addition, all switching apparatus and central office equipment frames are joined to the common ground system using large size copper cables.

A-C Ringing and Tone Generators

The principal equipment required in the central office to furnish ringing current for signaling subscriber stations is:

Rotary generators or ringing machines. Rotary generators or ringing machines consist of a single-speed motor (either ac or dc, depending on the power source) which drives, either directly or by pulleys and belts, one or more a-c generating units which produce the ringing frequencies.

Electronic oscillators. Electronic oscillators, employing vacuum tubes or solid-state devices, such as transistors and diodes, generate the required frequencies by tuned circuits. Motors or other moving parts are not necessary.

Magnetic generators. Magnetic generators operate from a-c mains. Resistors, transformers, and tuned circuits composed of inductors and capacitors create this form of static ringing generator. By subdividing and combining frequencies, an a-c output of one to five different frequencies can be produced.

Vibrating reed converter. A vibrating reed converter or frequency generator operates from the 48-volt central office battery. It is composed of two magnetic coils, an armature, and a reed assembly mounted on a frame. It converts the 48-volt dc to square-wave ac of the correct voltage for a particular output frequency. A filter circuit modifies the square-wave ac to a sine wave.

A mechanical interrupter normally breaks the ringing generator's output into ringing and silent periods. It is composed of a motor turning a number of cams on a drive shaft which operate contact springs to control the operation of relays that interrupt the ringing current into specified intervals. The ringing frequency output is to a distribution fuse panel on the powerboard by a twisted pair of leads. Alarm fuses installed on this panel protect the ringing supply.

Rotary interrupter cams also create the busy and ringback tone pulses. The low tone (480 Hz modulated by 620 Hz), for instance, is interrupted at the following rates to produce the indicated signals:

1. 60 impulses per minute (IPM) for called-line busy signal.
2. 30 IPM for intertoll-trunks busy signal.
3. 120 IPM for intra-office all-paths busy signal.

The tone generators required to produce the audio frequencies for dial tone, busy tone, ringback tone, etc. are of the same general types as described for the ringing generators. Dial tone, for example, is produced by a 480-Hz tone. Ringback tone is the 440-Hz tone modulated by 480-Hz tone.

Power and Equipment Fuse Alarms

Two general types of warning signals are provided in central offices for the power plant and switching equipment. *Major alarms* require immediate attention and quick action. *Minor alarms* usually indicate a trouble condition requiring less immediate attention. These alarms may be either instant or delayed types. The instant type of alarm is actuated at the moment the condition occurs, for example, a blown fuse. The delayed alarm, however, is not operative until a predetermined time period has elapsed. For instance, if all linefinders in a group should be busy, a delayed alarm usually would result. An instant alarm in this situation is not necessary because the all-busy condition may exist only momentarily.

Power apparatus and fuse alarms, whether of the major or minor type, require immediate attention. Central office d-c charging units usually are equipped with relays which release in the event of a power failure and high-voltage and low-voltage alarms which will function immediately if the battery voltage exceeds or falls below specified operating limits. In case of a commercial a-c power failure, an alarm-transfer relay will operate, signaling a major alarm condition. It also will transfer the ringing and tone generators and interrupters to alternate equipment. The successful operation of the alternate units will stop the immediate major alarm. If the standby equipment also should fail, both the immediate major and minor alarms will function.

Major power alarms include both main and distribution fuses on the powerboard. The blowing of any of these fuses will cause the associated parallel alarm fuse to blow. Figure 6-5 illustrates how the alarm fuse is connected across the main battery distributing fuses as used in the larger central offices. Two sets of fuses may be needed in parallel to handle the heavy battery current of the load. A large single-pole double-throw (SPDT) switch normally shorts one of the set of fuses. Therefore, if one set should blow, the second set can be immediately placed in service by operating the SPDT switch to the other position. The small indicating alarm fuse, in parallel with the main fuse, will blow simultaneously with the larger fuse, triggering the major alarm circuit.

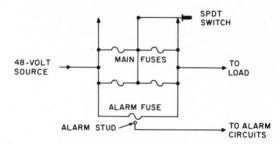

Figure 6-5   Main Power Fuse and Switch Arrangement with Alarm Fuse Connections

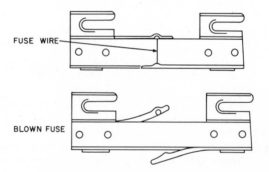

Figure 6-6   Alarm Indicating Fuse

The fuse panels associated with the various equipment shelves and frames of the central office switching equipment usually are equipped with alarm-indicating fuses. They are called "grasshopper" fuses and commonly are in the range of $1\frac{1}{3}$ to 5 amperes for either 24- or 48-volt operation. This type of fuse has two pretensioned springs which are held in place by the fuse wire. When the fuse wire blows, the two springs are released and bend away from the fuse element. The back spring will touch the alarm bar or stud to complete the circuit. A red lamp normally will light on the fuse panel to indicate the location of the blown fuse and within the fuse panel a front spring will bend upward locating the blown fuse. Figure 6-6 illustrates the construction of a typical alarm indicating fuse.

Review Questions

1. Name at least three types of electric power required in a central office.
2. In the event of a commercial power failure what is the primary power source in a central office?
3. What type of emergency power supply usually is provided in central offices?
4. What are the three main purposes of the central office battery?
5. How many cells comprise the central battery in the larger offices? What is the purpose of the end cells?
6. What type of equipment normally provides the 48-volt d-c supply in the average central office? What is the advantage?
7. What terminal of the central office battery usually is grounded?
8. Name three or more principal means of furnishing ringing current in the central office.
9. What two general classes of alarms are provided in central offices? What is a delayed alarm?
10. What is a "grasshopper" fuse? Describe it.

7

Step-By-Step Dial System

Elements of S × S System

While many of the important elements of the S × S dial system have been covered in preceding chapters, it is necessary to pull the system together for a better understanding of its operation. S × S switching continues to be an important system for, despite the many advancements in the use of common control switching, S × S central offices still outnumber the common control types.

The basic switch used in modern S × S systems is a two-motion stepping switch, the *Strowger switch*, named after its inventor. It is composed of a shaft which first is raised vertically and then rotated horizontally by a ratchet mechanism under the control of relays and an electromechanical device. Two sets of wipers, which can make contact with the bank terminals, are attached to the lower part of the shaft. Vertical and rotary stepping magnets are mounted on the switch frame and an electromagnet is provided to release the ratchet mechanism in order for the shaft to return to normal when the connection is released.

The apparatus used to establish connections in a S × S central office is called the *switch train* and is composed of a number of stepping switches. The first switch in the train is called the *linefinder*; the last switch is designated the *connector*. All intermediate switches are known as *selectors*. The amount of equipment required for a central office depends on the number of subscriber lines served and the calling rate during the busy-hour period. Other equipment may be added to the switch train, such as trunk equipment for handling interoffice calls. Figure 7-1 illustrates a local switch train in a S × S central office serving up to 10,000 subscribers. The selector switches for the office code (first three-digits) have been omitted and only the selector switches for the four-digit line number are shown.

The linefinder switch, always associated with a first selector, finds and connects to the calling line. Dial tone is sent by the first selector. The first digit dialed selects the particular thousand-group selector switch. The second digit directs the selection of the hundred group by the second selector, and the terminating switch or connector responds to the last two digits dialed, the tens and units of the called number. The connector then tests the called line and, if idle, applies ringing current. If the line is busy, the connector sends back the busy signal to the calling party.

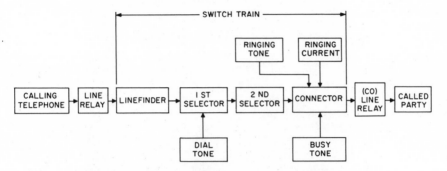

Figure 7-1   Step-By-Step Switch Train

Linefinder Equipment

The amount of connecting links in a dial office is designed to accommodate only a fraction of the subscriber lines at any one time. This arrangement is similar to manual central offices where the number of switchboard cord circuits is also very small in proportion to the number of lines served. Since there are only a few links as compared to the vast number of lines, the links may be considered to be in a pool for use as needed by originating subscribers.

The linefinder is the device which connects an idle link to a calling line. It is a hunting-type switch equipped with the necessary relays and bank terminals to serve up to 200 subscribers. Since it hunts for the calling line instead of being positioned by dial pulses, as are selectors and connectors, it is called a non-numerical switch.

A linefinder shelf serving 200 subscribers is composed of group relays, distributors, associated line relays, and linefinders as shown in Fig. 7-2. Each subscriber line circuit connects to the corresponding terminals on the banks of all linefinders on the shelf. While the number of linefinders required to serve 200 lines depends on the rate of busy-hour calling, 19 linefinders are usually assigned. However, if the originating traffic should require more equipment, another shelf equipped only with linefinders and banks may be added for use by the same 200 subscribers.

A linefinder normally requires a maximum of 20 steps to reach a calling line, 10 vertical and 10 rotary. When the bank's wiring is reversed, the average hunting time is reduced since all lines in the lower five levels can be reached with a maximum of 15 steps; 5 up and 10 across as illustrated in Fig. 7-3. A calling line, assigned to terminals in the 1-50 numbered sequence, will activate Group A relays to start a preselected Group A line-

Figure 7-2   Linefinder Shelf
courtesy of Automatic Electric Co.

finder to hunt for it. Similarly a calling line in the 51-100 series will acti-vate a Group B linefinder. If all A linefinders are busy, a B linefinder will be directed to hunt for the calling line.

Linefinder Operation

The prime function of a linefinder is to locate a calling line and con-nect it to the first selector of the switch train. As the subscriber lifts his handset, he initiates this action. Following a typical subscriber line cir-cuit in Fig. 7-4, note that the (L) relay first operates through the nor-mal contacts of its associated (CO) relay and over the closed subscriber loop which results from the off-hook condition. The operation of (L) initi-ates the following actions:

1. It grounds the S lead to make the particular line test busy to any incoming calls at the connectors.

2. It connects the battery through the winding of (CO) to mark the subscriber line CF terminal on the linefinder banks.

3. It grounds the start-ST-and vertical level-LEV-leads which causes a preselected linefinder to hunt for the calling line and places a ground on

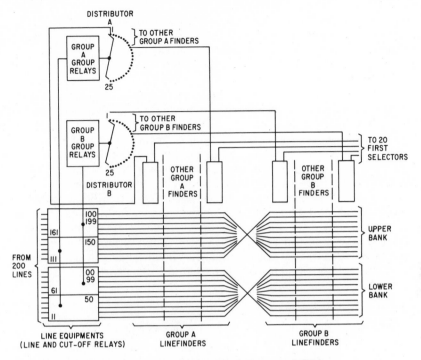

Figure 7-3   Linefinder-Bank Reversal Wiring

the vertical level of the linefinder bank in which the calling line is located.

The linefinder first steps vertically until it contacts the bank level containing the calling line as indicated by ground on its LEV lead. The rotary magnets rotate the shaft until the wipers contact the terminals of the calling line as shown by battery on the CF lead. Once the linefinder connects to the calling line, CF will be grounded, operating (CO) in the line circuit

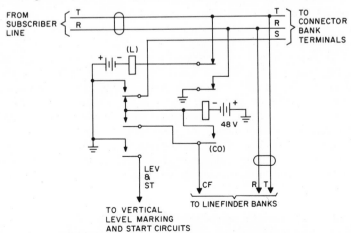

Figure 7-4   Subscriber-Line Relay Circuit

which locks to the CF lead and removes (L) from its connection to the calling line as shown by battery on the CF lead. Once the linefinder connects linefinder control circuits are advanced. With the linefinder connected to the terminals of the calling line, a circuit is closed to extend the T, R, and S leads of the calling line to the first selector which was previously associated with the particular linefinder. The first selector holds operated the linefinder control relay and the (CO) relay in the line circuit. Dial tone will then be supplied by the first selector to the calling subscriber.

When the calling subscriber hangs up at the completion of a call, the various selector and connector switches release. The release of the first selector removes ground from the S lead and releases the (CO) relay in the line circuit. Removal of ground from the S lead permits the particular line to receive incoming calls. The release of (CO) serves to reconnect (L) across the subscriber line. At the same time, the linefinder release magnet will operate. The shaft and wipers of the linefinder rotate counterclockwise and then drop to their normal position, causing the vertical off-normal contacts to open the release-magnet circuit as an indication that the linefinder is restored to normal and is ready to be seized for another call.

Selector Switch

The selectors in the switch train are two-motion switches which are directly actuated by the dial pulses. The shaft of the selector first is raised vertically under direct control of the pulses of the dialed digit, selecting the desired trunk level or thousandths group. The rotary motion which follows, is the automatic trunk-hunting movement of the selector switch. It selects an idle path to the next selector switch, which is wired to the selected vertical level. Except for the vertical stepping, which is controlled by the dialing, operations of the selector switch are automatic, including the release actions which occur after the calling party hangs up.

The major functions of a selector are:

1. It holds operated all preceding switches in the switch train immediately upon seizure.

2. It selects the desired vertical level in response to the particular digit dialed.

3. It finds and connects with an idle trunk on the selected vertical level by rotary motion.

Figure 7 - 5 illustrates a typical selector switch. It is usually composed of a frame which supports a shaft and its stepping magnets and five control relays mounted on a base. A ratchet mechanism for raising and lowering the shaft is attached to the frame. The lower portion of the shaft has two wipers or contact arms designated *control* and *line* wipers which can engage terminals on the semicylindrical banks attached to the bottom of the selector. The upper bank is the control bank and the lower one is the line bank. A latch with two detents holds the shaft and wipers in the position to which they have been stepped by the vertical and rotary movements of the selector switch until released by the action of the release magnet.

The rotary motion of the selector first tests the trunks on the selected vertical level in successive order and stops the rotary motion at the first idle trunk. It disconnects the line bank wipers during the rotation movement and holds busy the selected trunk until the holding circuit is completed by the succeeding selector in the switch train or by the connector switch. It then extends the T and R line terminals to the next switch in the train and disconnects all relays from this talking path. If all trunks in the selected vertical level are busy, an audible busy signal will be returned to the calling party. When the party hangs up, the selector releases.

There are two basic types of selector circuits in the switch train. Both select an idle trunk during the trunk-hunting or rotary motion period of the selector. The absence-of-ground-hunting selector searches for a no-ground condition on the C or S terminal as an indication of an idle trunk or selector. The *battery-hunting* selector searches for a battery potential on the C or S terminal as the identification of an idle trunk. Busy trunks in both types of selectors are marked by ground on the C or S lead.

Figure 7 - 5   Selector
courtesy of Automatic Electric Co.

Selector Operations

The complete schematic circuit of a typical battery-hunting selector is shown in Fig. 7-6. Note that the five relays are designated (F), (A), (B), (C) and (D), and that their respective spring contacts are drawn in a vertical row above or below the respective relay. The vertical dash lines indicate the contact springs associated with each relay. The essential circuit operations in Fig. 7-6 are that of a second selector which is also typical of the other switches in the switch train. Note that an idle second selector has battery through the 500-ohm winding of its (C) relay connected to the C or S lead on the preceding first selector control bank.

When the idle second selector is seized by the first selector during trunk hunting, (C) operates to ground on the C lead from the first selector circuit. Subsequently, the T and R leads (the talking path of the calling subscriber line) are connected from the particular first selector and its associated linefinder switch to the second selector circuit. Relay (A) now operates over the calling party loop circuit through the normally closed contacts of the (F) relay. Contacts 2-3 of the operated (A) relay will complete the operating circuit of relay (B), which is a slow-release type.

With the (B) relay operated, ground on its contacts 6-7 is connected to the C lead to hold the preceding first selector circuit. This same ground also operates (C) through its 500-ohm winding and contacts 5-6 of the vertical-off-normal (VON) springs. In addition, ground on contacts 8-9 of relay (B) causes the operation of the supervisory (SUPV) relay in the shelf equipment. With the (SUPV) relay operated, the PERM. SIG. lamp lights as an indication that a selector on the particular shelf has been seized.

As the subscriber dials the second digit, relay (A) releases during each open period of the dial contacts, completing a circuit through its released contacts 2-1 and operated contacts 2-3 of relay (B) to operate the vertical magnet in series with the 5-ohm winding of the (C) relay. Relay (B), a slow-release type with a copper sleeve on its core, will not fall down during the momentary release periods of the (A) relay.

The operation of the vertical magnet lifts the shaft one step so that its wipers are on the first level of the bank terminals. Each successive dial pulse causes the reoperation of the vertical magnet, thus raising the shaft another step to the next vertical level. For example, dialing the digit 5 causes the shaft to be elevated to the fifth vertical level, releasing the *vertical-off-normal* (VON) springs mechanically. Relay (D) next operates through a circuit which includes cam springs 1-2, (F) relay normal contacts 1-2, (B) relay operated contacts 10-11, and VON contacts 5-6 to ground on the C lead from the preceding first selector. Also, VON contacts 5-6 open the operating circuit of (C) but it does not release because, being a slow-release type, it is held through its 5-ohm winding under control of (A). Relay (C), therefore, remains operated during the dial pulsing operations which release and operate (A). Note in Fig. 7-6 that (A) in the selector circuit is operated directly by the closure of the calling subscriber loop. It releases and reoperates under direct control of the dial pulses. If the calling subscriber should be at a considerable distance from the central office, the

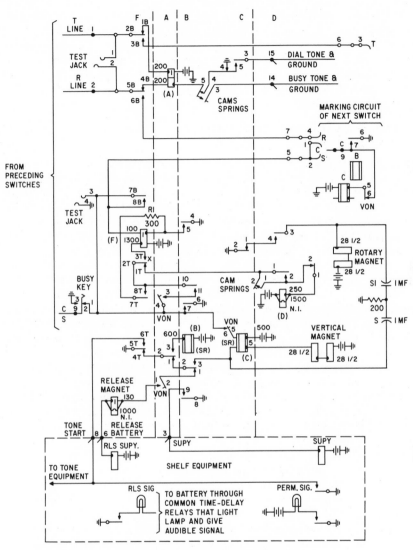

Figure 7-6   A Selector Circuit

increased line resistance limits the current flow through the windings of the (A) relay. Therefore, (A) will be weakly magnetized and will release quickly when the dial contact springs open. Similarly, it will reoperate slowly when the dial contacts reclose. As a result, (C) receives an extra long pulse.

On the other hand, a subscriber station near the central office produces a larger current flow through (A), thereby strongly magnetizing it. Under this condition, (A) releases slowly and reoperates quickly under control of the dial pulses, resulting in a short pulse to (C).

To neutralize these conditions, relays (A) and (C) are mounted adjacent to each other on the selector frame so that their magnetic fields interact. Thus, when (A) is magnetized only moderately on a long subscriber loop, the magnetic flux from (C) assists the operation of (A). Moreover, when (A) is strongly magnetized by a short subscriber loop, so that the pulse to (C) is short, the strong flux of (A) will help to maintain (C) operated between dial pulses.

Trunk Selection Operations

Upon completion of the five dial pulses comprising the second digit dialed, (A) remains operated over the subscriber loop and (C) releases. With (C) released, ground through its spring contacts 2-1 and operated contacts 4-3 of relay (D) operates the rotary magnet rotating the shaft and its wipers clockwise to the first set of bank terminals on the previously selected, fifth vertical level. These bank terminals correspond to trunk 1. As the rotary magnet armature completes its operation, rotary interrupter contacts 1-2 open to release the (D) relay.

If trunk 1 is busy, there will be a ground on the C contacts of the control bank and relay (F) will not operate. In the meantime, the release of (D) opens the operating circuit of the rotary magnet which starts to release. As it does, its interrupter contacts 1-2 reclose the operating circuit for (D). This rotary stepping cycle is repeated either until an idle trunk is found, as indicated by a battery potential on the C lead, or all ten trunks on the particular vertical level test busy.

An idle trunk is marked by negative resistance battery (from the (C) relay circuit in the succeeding selector or connector circuit) on the C lead. This battery condition on the C lead energizes the 100-ohm winding of (F). As (F) operates it locks up through its 1300-ohm winding, spring contacts 3T-2T, contacts 10-11 of the operated (B) relay, VON contacts 3-4, to ground on make contacts 7-6 of operated (B). It should be noted that contacts 2T-3T of (F) close before its other contacts, insuring that the locking circuit for the 1300-ohm winding of (F) is closed before the ground at (B) contacts 6-7 short-circuits the 100-ohm winding of relay (F).

The operation of relay (F) releases (A) and closes through the calling party's line to the next switch in the switch train over the T and R wiper leads. The combined time for (A) and (B) to operate in the next switch circuit is much less than the release time of (B) in this second selector circuit. Therefore, (F) is held operated over the C lead from the succeeding switch before the release of (B) opens the circuit to ground at contacts 6-7. The release of (B) removes the short circuit across the 100-ohm winding of (F). The current through the 100-ohm winding is in an opposite direction than that through the 1300-ohm winding. This situation makes (F) quick releasing at the end of the call when the calling subscriber disconnects.

If all ten trunks on the fifth vertical level should test busy, the shaft will be revolved to the eleventh terminal, causing cam springs 1-2 to open so that relay (D) will not operate after the eleventh terminal is reached. At the same time, cam springs 3-5 make and 4-5 break, replacing direct ground connection to the (A) winding with a ground through the busy-

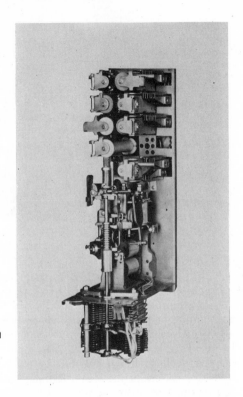

Figure 7-7   Connector Switch

courtesy of Automatic Electric Co.

tone transformer. In this manner, an all-trunks-busy (ATB) signal is sent to the calling subscriber.

When the calling party hangs up at the completion of the call, relay (A) in the connector circuit—the last switch in the switch train—will be released first. The corresponding relay (B) in the connector circuit next releases and ground is removed from the C or S lead back to the second selector circuit. Removal of ground on the C lead releases (F) which initiates the restoring of the second selector. The release magnet now operates through vertical off-normal (VON) contacts 1-2, normal contacts 1-2 of the (B) and (A) relays, to ground on contacts 4T-5T of the normal (F). With the release magnet operating, its armature strikes the latch which disengages its two detents from the vertical and rotary ratchets. The shaft, therefore, is returned to its normal position, but just before reaching this position, the VON springs 1-2 open to break the operating path of the release magnet. Simultaneously, VON springs 5-6 reconnect battery through the 500-ohm winding of the (C) relay to the C lead as an indication of an idle switch.

Connector Switch

The last switch in the step-by-step switch train is the connector. It responds to the last two digits dialed—the tens and units—of the called number. The connector, shown in Fig. 7-7, is similar to the selector in appear-

Figure 7-8 Typical Connector Shelf

courtesy of Automatic Electric Co.

ance and circuit operations. Usually assembled in rows of 9 or 11 switches called shelves, connectors provide connections to 100 line numbers through two banks of contacts (see Fig. 7-8). Both banks of contacts have ten levels; the lower bank is a 200-point type which has two contacting surfaces in each position for the T and R transmission leads. The upper bank has 100 bridging contacts for the control leads which are usually designated C or S. This type of connector is considered a 300-point bank.

The principal functions of a connector are:

1. To select the called line number from the tens and units digits dialed.
2. To test the line for an idle or busy indication.
3. To apply ringing current and to return ringback tone to the calling party, if the called line is idle.
4. To return busy tone to the calling party if the line tests busy.
5. To supply talking battery to both the calling and called party when the called party answers (reverse-battery supervision).
6. To provide a ground on the C or S lead to hold operated the entire switch train for the duration of the call.

To perform these functions, a total of eight relays are provided in the connector circuit. A number of these relays perform the same functions as their counterparts in the selector circuit. Figure 7-9 illustrates the circuitry of these eight relays. The contact springs associated with each relay are shown above or below. The operations of these relays are considered rather than studying the circuit as a whole since many relay operations are similar to the selector circuit.

Connector relay (A) is operated over the calling-party loop and closes a circuit to operate relay (B) through its contacts 2-3. (A) follows the dial pulses of the last two digits and directs the vertical and rotary stepping operations of the connector. Slow-release relay (B) is controlled by (A) and

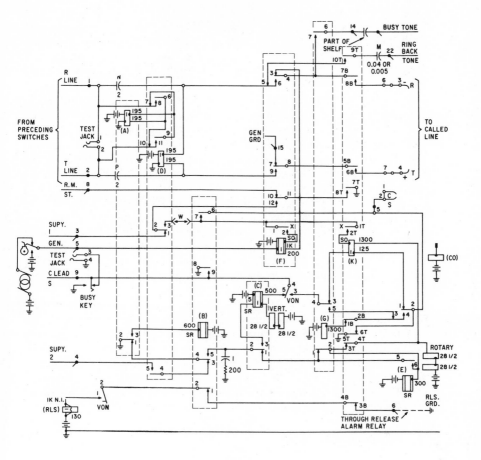

Figure 7-9 Connector Circuit

serves to hold operated the preceding switches in the switch train. Relay (C), which operated over the C lead when the connector was originally seized, is also a slow-release type. It releases during the interdigital pause between the dialing of the tens and units and prepares the circuit for stepping the rotary magnet. Relay (E) operates during the rotary motion of the connector when the units are dialed. It also is a slow-release relay and remains operated long enough after completion of rotary stepping to permit the connector circuit to test the called line for an idle or busy condition. Assume that in Fig. 7-9 the called line is busy as indicated by a ground on the C lead. The (G) relay operates through the normal 1B-2B contacts of (K) and operated contacts 4-2 of (E) to the C lead ground. In this example, operation of relay (G) prevents the operation of (K) and sends a busy tone through the operated contacts of 6-7 to the calling subscriber.

If the called line number is idle, there is negative battery on the C lead from the (CO) relay of the called line and the (CO) and (K) relays operate. With (K) operated, the T and R leads are closed through to the called line terminals. Ringing current is then applied to the called line through the 200-ohm winding of (F) and its normal made contacts 3-4, operated contacts 7B-8B of (K) over the R of the line to the called party and back over the T side of the line, operated contacts 6B-5B of (K) and through normal made contacts 8-7 of the (F) relay to the generator ground. At the same time, ring-back tone is returned to the calling subscriber through the operated contacts 9T-10T of (K), normal contacts 5-6 of (F), capacitor N in the R lead and back through the previous switches in the switch train to the calling party. Ground is supplied over the T lead through relay (A) winding and normal contacts 10-11 of relay (D).

When the called party answers, relay (F) operates over the line closure from the called party and its 1000-ohm winding locks to ground on the C lead. Operation of (F) removes ringing current from the called line and closes the circuit for operating relay (D). (D) supplies talking battery to the called party and also reverses the battery polarity supplied to the calling party by (A). This battery reversal is accomplished by the make-before-break contacts 6-8-7 and 9-11-10 of relay (D).

Talking-battery reversal is also known as *answer supervision*. It performs a number of important functions:

1. It results in the collection of coins deposited on a call from a coin box or pay station telephone.

2. It provides an off-hook signal to the operator on a call originated on a switchboard.

3. It causes the equipment to time the length of the call and determine the charges on long distance or toll calls.

Transmission Path

When the called party answers, the connector circuit advances to establish a transmission path between the calling and called parties through the switch train. This talking path is known as a two-wire transmission circuit because it requires 2 conductors, the T and R leads. Essentially this circuit is composed of the T and R leads of all the switches comprising the switch train. Figure 7-10 illustrates the basic talking path through a typical switch train in a local S × S central office. Note that capacitors N and P permit the passage of voice currents but separate the respective battery voltages supplied to the calling and called lines.

In the diagram, the voice currents from the calling party follow previously selected paths through the bank terminals of the linefinder, first and second selectors to the connector circuit. This path was chosen by the first two digits of the dialed number. In addition to the contacts on the linefinder and selector banks, observe that the talking path also goes through (A) contacts in the linefinder and the contacts of the (F) relays in the first and second selector circuits.

In the connector circuit, the voice currents readily go through the N and P capacitors in series with the R and T leads, respectively. The windings of the (A) and (D) relays offer a high impedance to the voice currents and will therefore impede their passage. The voice currents, accordingly, continue through the contacts of the operated (F) and (K) in the connector circuit to the particular bank terminals that were selected by dialing the last two digits. The voice currents from the called party follow the same route in the reverse order.

As indicated in the figure, the only relay windings connected across the transmission path are (A) and (D) of the connector circuit. Relay (A) supplies transmission battery to the calling party while the relay (D) does the same thing for the called party. Relay (A) also holds operated relay (B), which maintains a ground on the C or S lead of the connector. This ground holds operated the (F) relays in the selector circuits, the linefinder (A) relay and the calling-party (CO) relay over the C lead or control path of the switch train. This ground also marks the calling party's line busy on the banks of all connectors on which it appears. Similarly, the operated (K) relay in the connector maintains ground on the S lead to hold operated the called party's (CO) in the line circuit and to make busy the line on the connector banks.

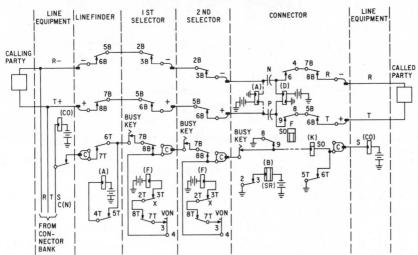

Figure 7-10   Switch Train Transmission Path

Disconnection of Switch Train

The release of the switch train in the typical S × S central office is under control of the connector circuit. In turn, the connector normally is designed to release when the calling party hangs up. For example, if the called party should hang up first, the (D) relay in the connector releases. However, referring to Fig. 7-9, the (A) and (B) relays of the connector still remain operated. Therefore, nothing further can occur until (A) is released when the calling party disconnects. However, a timed-release circuit may be provided to release the connector in case the calling party should fail to hang up within a prescribed interval (40 to 60 seconds) after the called

**Figure 7 - 11   Rotary and Vertical Bank Assembly of
Digit-Absorbing Selector**
courtesy of Automatic Electric Co.

party disconnects. This arrangement frees the called line which, otherwise, would be held busy.

When the calling party hangs up first, relay (A) immediately releases causing the operation of relay (E) and opening the operating path of the slow-release (B). When (B) releases, ground is removed from the C or S lead which permits all preceding switches in the switch train to restore to their normal positions. With relay (B) normal, slow-release (E) releases and a ground is placed on the C or S lead to mark the connector busy. As soon as the called party disconnects, (D) relay releases and the holding circuits of the (F) and (K) relays are opened.

The release of relay (K) opens the T, R and S leads of the connector's wipers and closes the circuit, operating the release magnet. With the release magnet energized, the connector shaft rotates counterclockwise and away from its bank terminals. The weight of the shaft restores it to normal, allowing the VON springs 1 - 2 to open the circuit of the release magnet. At the same time, VON springs 4 - 5 connect 500-ohm battery from the (C) relay winding to the C lead as an indication of an idle connector.

Digit-Absorbing Selector

The description of S × S switch train operations assumes a local call within the central office requiring only the four digits of the called line. Calls to other central offices, as in multi-office areas, necessitate the dialing of all seven digits. It is not necessary, however, to provide three additional selectors, one for handling each digit of the office code, in order to handle such calls. In many small communities, the single central office may serve only a few thousand subscribers, needing only about two to five levels on the first selector for the first or thousands digit of any local number. The other vertical levels may be used for operator assistance calls—0, toll access—1 and calls to other central offices in the same or extended service area.

When three-digit office codes are dialed but only one or two digits are necessary to select a trunk to another central office, or if dialing the office code is not required on local calls, a digit-absorbing selector is used. This type of selector is very similar to the usual first selector except that it contains two more relays (usually designated (D) and (Z)) and an extra ten-point vertical bank assembly. In addition, a set of normal post springs (NPS) are included to prevent incorrect dialing sequence. This type of selector can be arranged to absorb the first, the first two, or the first three digits. A digit is absorbed by the return of the switch shaft to its normal position after first stepping to the vertical level corresponding to the digit dialed. The next digit will again step the switch vertically. However, if this digit is not to be absorbed, the selector's rotary magnet will hunt for an idle trunk to the called office or select a path to another selector switch.

The ten-point vertical bank assembly, Fig. 7-11, is used in a digit-absorbing selector. The digit-absorbing operations depend upon the particular cross-connections that are made from the ten-point vertical bank to its associated terminal block. The nine terminals on this block are wired to the contact springs of the (Z) relay and to the CI, A and AR leads, see Fig. 7-12. The figure illustrates how these cross-connections and the (D) and (Z) relays control the actions of the digit-absorbing selector. For example, if numbers 1 to 4 and 0 of the first digit dialed are not to be absorbed, the CI or cut-in lead is connected to the corresponding vertical bank terminals 1, 2, 3, 4 and 0. Now, should the first digit be one of these numbers, a circuit will be closed to fully operate (D) with both of its windings in series. Therefore, when (C) releases at the completion of the dialed digit, ground from the operated contacts 10-11 of (B) through the released springs 3-4 of (C) through relay (E) normal contacts 6-5, through the left normal post springs 1-2, through the vertical bank wiper terminal 1 and over the CI lead to fully operate (D) through its two windings in series. With (D) fully operated, the rotary magnet circuit is closed and the shaft rotates to select an idle path.

To only absorb the first digit dialed, but to permit the selector to cut in on any succeeding digit, the A lead is connected to the particular vertical bank terminal. In this case, upon the release of relay (C) at the completion of the digit, a circuit closes to only the 175-ohm winding of (D). Relay (D) can operate only partially under this condition so that just the X contacts 1-2 and 3-4 will be closed. With X contacts 1-2 closed, the release magnet restores the switch shaft to its normal position. The (Z) relay now operates removing dial tone and ground from the calling line. At the same time, the short circuit around the 450-ohm winding of (D) is removed so that it will fully operate and lock up. The selector switch is then ready to receive

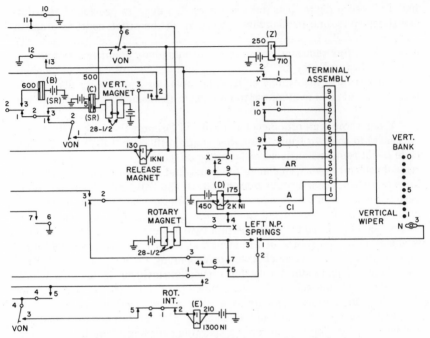

Figure 7-12   Simplified Digit-Absorbing Selector

the pulses of the next digit. When (C) relay releases at the end of the pulsing of the next digit, a circuit is closed through contacts 6-7 of fully operated (D) to actuate the rotary magnet in order to hunt for an idle path. The release magnet cannot operate at this time because contacts 8-9 of (D) relay will be opened.

If a particular digit is to be repeatedly absorbed, the AR lead is wired to the vertical bank terminal associated with the desired level. The AR lead connection operates the release magnet when the (C) relay falls down upon completion of vertical stepping. If an AR lead-connected digit should follow a lead A connected digit, the digit associated with the AR lead will be cut in. This results because the (D) relay was previously operated and locked by the circuit of the A lead connection. Therefore, the rotary magnet will operate on any subsequent dialed digit to select an idle path. In general, whenever a digit causes the partial operation of (D), that digit will be absorbed because the release magnet operates. If a dialed digit results in (D) operating fully, the rotary magnet will be operated instead of the release magnet to select an idle trunk or path.

It also is possible to provide two markings on a level through optional strapping of a vertical bank. For example, assume that the first digit 3 and the second digit 3 are to be absorbed but that the third digit, whether 3 or any other number, is to be cut in. Leads AR and A are used for this purpose. In this situation, lead AR which is connected to terminal 3 on the terminal block, is strapped to terminal 4. Similarly, lead A, which is wired to terminal

2, would be strapped to terminal 6. Vertical bank level 3 would be connected to terminal 5. When the first digit 3 is dialed, the AR lead connection, with the (Z) relay normal, causes the operation of the release magnet. Upon restoration of the selector shaft to normal, (Z) will operate, removing dial tone and ground from the calling line. The A lead is then connected to the 3 level instead of the AR lead by the operated contacts 8-9 of the (Z) relay. Therefore, the second digit 3 is absorbed but (D) will be fully operated. As a result, when the third digit 3 is dialed, the rotary magnet will function to select an idle path and cut in the selector.

Review Questions

1. What is the fundamental switch used in step-by-step switching systems? Describe its basic operations.
2. What essential elements of a switch train are used for a local call? Which switches are designed to automatically hunt for idle paths?
3. What are the major functions of a selector switch?
4. What relays in a selector circuit are always mounted adjacent to each other? Why?
5. How are idle and busy trunks indicated on the selector banks?
6. What are some principal functions of the connector?
7. What is the purpose of answer supervision?
8. What circuit controls the release of the switch train in a S × S central office? What party must hang up to disconnect the call? Why?
9. What is the purpose of the digit-absorbing selector?
10. How are the digits absorbed by the digit-absorbing selector?

8

Crossbar and Other Common-Control Switching Systems

Electromechanical Dial Switching Systems

The panel type switching technique, reviewed in Chapter 5, was developed by the Bell System shortly after World War I. The first panel dial offices were installed during the 1920's in the larger metropolitan cities to replace manual central offices. Trial installations of a rotary system also were made during this period but the Bell System decided to standardize on the panel dial system within the United States. The rotary switching system was further developed in Europe, particularly by the Bell Manufacturing Company of Antwerp, Belgium, an affiliate of the International Telephone and Telegraph Corporation. It was designated the *7-A Rotary System*. Installations of this system have been made in many countries of Europe and in other parts of the world, and some installations have been made for Independent Telephone companies in the U.S.

The panel and rotary systems generally follow the same design principles but employ different types of power-driven switch frames. The panel system uses straight vertical banks with selectors on both sides to contact the desired terminals while the rotary system utilizes semicircular banks. Both systems employ power-driven sequence switches and incorporate equivalent common-control apparatus, such as register-senders, translators and link finders.

The high maintenance costs of power-driven mechanisms, the use of sliding contacts, and the relatively long time required for the various selectors to complete calls are the prime disadvantages of the panel system. These and other factors led to the development of a switching system based upon the crossbar switch. In the United States, the first such switching system designed by Bell was the *No. 1 Crossbar*. Initial installations were made in New York and other large cities just prior to World War II. The present version, the *No. 5 Crossbar,* is capable of operating with all present local, tandem, and toll switching systems of Bell System and Independent Telephone companies. It provides about the ultimate in sophisticated electromechanical switching systems.

A similar system, known as the Pentaconta Crossbar System, was developed in France after World War II by the Compagnie General de Construction Teléphoniques (CGCT), a subsidiary of International Telephone and Télégraph Corporation. This common-control system is extensively used in Europe and recently was introduced in the United States. It utilizes a type of crossbar switch, the Pentaconta, which has 28 select magnets and 22 hold magnets. The Western Electric crossbar switch has 10 select and 20 hold magnets. The design and operating principles of both crossbar systems are basically equivalent.

The operations of common-control techniques as applied to the S × S systems will be considered first because of important similarities. The No. 5 Crossbar and the power-driven panel systems will follow.

Common Control for S × S Offices

Means for applying common-control techniques to step-by-step (S × S) offices had been known for a long time. But, until recently, these steps were not considered to be economical nor essential for most applications. However, the advent of direct distance dialing (DDD), assignment of seven-digit numbers to all subscriber lines, extended area service (EAS), and the need for alternate routing of outgoing traffic and other factors have changed the picture. A number of improved methods have been developed that incorporate common-control and translation features into existing S × S central offices without modification of the switches in the switch train. The electromechanical *register-sender* is the essential element of this common-control application.

Some of the advantages of common-control functions to S × S offices include:

1. The elimination of the need for digit-absorbing selectors.

2. The provision for multifrequency (MF) signaling to other common control offices, such as the No. 5 Crossbar.

3. The provision of alternate routings via other central office trunks or through tandem centers to carry overflow traffic.

4. The provision of pushbutton calling in place of dials at subscriber stations.

One method for merging common-control features into existing S × S offices is the *101 Director System* that has been developed by Automatic Electric Co. This system provides:

1. Access equipment to enable the register-sender to be connected to present S × S equipment without modification of any selector switches.

2. Register-sender apparatus of the electromechanical type to receive, store, and convert the dial pulses received from subscriber stations into codes for subsequent translation and control of the switch train.

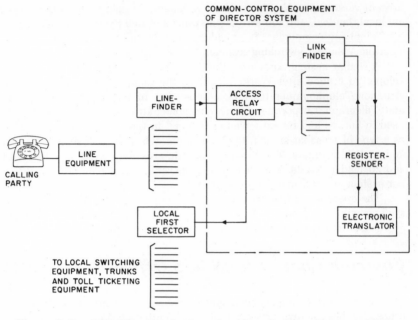

Figure 8-1   101 Director System for Step-By-Step Central Office

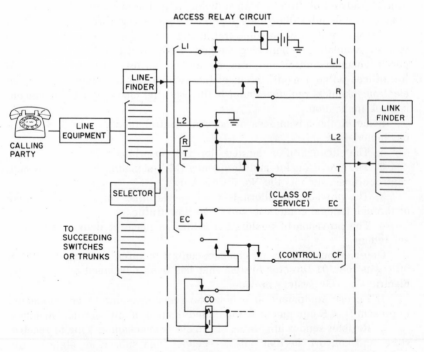

Figure 8-2   Access Relay Circuit of 101 Director System

3. An electronic translator unit, which may be common to as many as 100 register-senders, that contains routing instructions in its logic circuits for handling all types of calls.

The main elements of the *101 Director System* as applied to a typical S × S central office are illustrated in Fig. 8-1. They consist of the *access relay circuit, link finder, register-sender* and its associated electronic *translator.* One access relay circuit is associated with each linefinder unit and is inserted between the linefinder and the selector of the switch train. The access relay circuit serves to extend the subscriber dialing loop leads to the link finder for connection to the register-sender. In addition, the link finder connects the T and R control leads, or pulsing path, from the register-sender to the first selector and the succeeding switches in the switch train. In effect, the access relay circuit splits the connection from the calling party to the first selector until the common-control equipment completes its operations and releases. See Fig. 8-2.

The link finder circuit functions in a similar manner as a linefinder and normally serves up to 100 access relay circuits. It is activated by the access relay circuit on an originating call. After finding the particular access relay circuit, the link finder closes the subscriber line to the register-sender. At the same time, it connects the register-sender outgoing T and R control leads to the access relay circuit and to the first selector for subsequent outpulsing into the switch train. The class-of-service or EC lead also is extended to the register-sender if this feature is provided. Figure 8-3 shows this interface. Dial tone is sent to the calling party, however, by the register-sender instead of from the first selector. Since the link finder is activated at nearly the same time as the linefinder circuit, the subscriber will receive dial tone in about the same time interval.

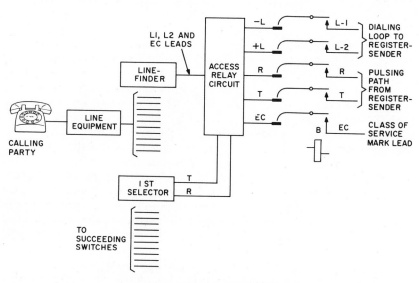

Figure 8-3   Link Finder Circuit

Register-Sender Functions in S ✕ S Office

The digits dialed by the originating subscriber are recorded on a chain of counting relays within the register-sender. During each interdigital pause, the recorded digit (whose dial pulses had been counted) is converted to a two-out-of-five code and stored on another set of special reed-type relays known as *codelreed*. A codelreed consists of a steel reed over which two wire coils have been wound. Two such units are then encapsulated with a permanent magnet between them, designed not to cause the operation of the reed contacts but to hold them operated whenever current flows through the coils. The codelreed will remain operated until the two windings are energized by opposing currents. Only five codelreeds are required to store any digit by using the two-out-of-five code shown in Fig. 8-4. For example, the code for the digit 2 is 1-3, and the code for digit 9 is 3-5. The two-out-of-five code also provides a parity check because two codelreeds must be operated to indicate that a valid digit has been stored. If one, three or more codelreeds should operate, a trouble condition will be indicated by the register-sender. See Fig. 8-5.

Two-Out-of-Five Code Table

Digit Dialed	Codelreed Relays Operated	Digit Dialed	Codelreed Relays Operated
1	#1 and #2	6	#3 and #4
2	#1 and #3	7	#1 and #5
3	#2 and #3	8	#2 and #5
4	#1 and #4	9	#3 and #5
5	#2 and #4	0	#4 and #5

Figure 8-4

The stored digits are presented to the translator in the same two-out-of-five code. The translator transforms the received information into instructions, sent back to the register-sender, which control the outpulsing and holding of the switch train during the progress of the call. These instructions are sent to the register-sender in the form of a two-or-three-out-of-five code of timed negative battery pulses. The register-sender can be directed to perform functions such as repeating the next dialed digit, releasing the first and second selectors so that the first two dialed digits can be absorbed, and directing these selectors for alternate routings.

For example, presume all ten trunks to a certain central office appearing on level 2 of the second selector are busy and alternate routes are provided. The (ATB) relay in the register-sender will operate. Upon recognizing that an alternate routing is required, the register-sender first releases the first and second selectors by momentarily opening the T and R loop, and then it directs the first and second selector switches to other levels (such as 4 and 3, respectively) to select an idle alternate routing trunk. The translator had previously sent this indicated information to the register-sender.

The translator actually is a high-speed electronic device utilizing a

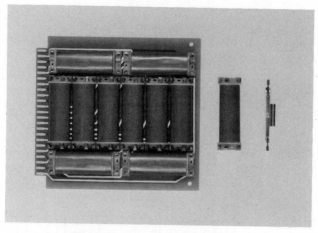

Figure 8-5   Codelreed Relays

Codelreed relays are used in the register-sender of
the 101 Director. Components of a codelreed are
shown on the right.

courtesy of Automatic Electric Co.

time division access method to serve up to 100 register-senders. The translator can receive a maximum of six digits (area and office codes) for translation and provide the necessary routing instructions to the register-sender within a time interval of 100 microseconds. All register-senders associated with the same translator are individually connected to the latter in
sequence over several common leads. The translator, therefore, is continu-
ally scanning all register-senders to determine when a dialed code requires
translation. It will return the translated information to the register-sender
as soon as the dialed code has been registered, whether that code consists
of one or up to six digits.

Multifrequency (MF) tone pulsing often is used for toll or DDD calls.
Each register-sender must be equipped with an MF control circuit for this
purpose. Figure 8-6 illustrates the use of the register-sender for local calls.
When an area or office code routing requires MF sending, the translator
will instruct the register-sender to delay outpulsing until all digits are dialed
and stored. After the last digit is recorded, the register-sender will direct
the first and second selectors to seize an outgoing trunk to the desired office. The translator then will operate the (MF) relay in the register-sender to cause it to outpulse the stored digits in the MF mode. The register-sender normally repeats the first digit dialed to the first selector. For local calls,
however, it is usually necessary to absorb the first two digits of the office
code because only the third digit of the office code is used for directing
the first selector to the proper level to select an idle path to the other switches in the switch train. Follow the register-sender's functions on a local call
when the office code 335 for called number 335-1234 is dialed. The register-sender immediately repeats the first digit 3 to the first selector.
The translator, recognizing that the first digit 3 may indicate a local call,
orders the register-sender to release the first selector. When the second

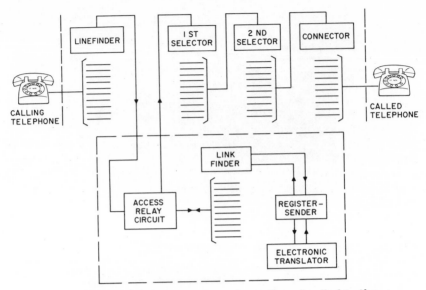

Figure 8-6   **Common-Control Operations Applied to the Step-By-Step Central Office**

digit 3 is dialed, the code 33 is sent to the translator, which recognizes it as the elements of a local call. The register-sender, therefore, will be directed to repeat the next dialed digit to the first selector. In effect, the second digit 3 was absorbed within the register-sender. As soon as the third digit 5 is dialed, it is repeated by the register-sender directly to the first selector as ordered by the translator. At the same time, the digits 335 will be sent to the translator by the register-sender in its particular time slot. The translator now will initiate the release of the register-sender. The other selectors in the switch train subsequently will be directly controlled by the four digits of the called line number, 1234, as they are dialed. Subsequent operations and disconnection follow the same procedure as in normal S × S central offices.

Panel Switching System

The main switching elements for establishing connections between customers in the panel system are the five types of selector frames which are designated *linefinder, district, office, incoming,* and *final.* The linefinder, district, and office frames handle the outgoing calls. The incoming and final frames complete connections to the called numbers. The principal common-control devices are the register-sender and its associated *decoder* or *decoder marker* circuit. The register-sender temporarily stores the pulses received from the calling party's dial and calls in a decoder to translate the first three digits (area or office code) into proper routing information. These are sent back to the register-sender for subsequent control of the district, office, incoming, and final selections. Another important component is the *district-sender link* frame which connects idle district selectors to linefinder circuits. This link circuit also connects an idle register-sender to the linefinder-district circuit on an originating call. See Fig. 8-7.

In the S × S system, recall that the operation of the subscriber line relay caused a linefinder switch to connect itself to the calling-line bank terminals. The linefinder has a first selector directly connected to it. In the panel system the operation of the subscriber line relay likewise causes a linefinder selector to find the calling line. The linefinder also is directly connected to a district selector. In addition, a register-sender is connected to the subscriber line through the district and the district-sender link frame. The dialed digits are recorded in the register-sender which then calls in a decoder to translate the area or office code. The decoder translates the area or office code into particular brush and group selections for the district and office selectors. The register-sender then sets up the call through the district, office, incoming, and final selectors to the called line. As soon as these selections are completed, the register-sender is released. The selections are controlled over the trunk conductors which are used later for speech transmission. The revertive pulse counting method, using ground pulses originated by the selectors, is the technique employed for this control function.

The subscriber lines in the panel system are connected to terminals on the linefinder and final banks of the frames in a similar manner as in the S × S system. In fact, the linefinder frames perform the same functions as the linefinder switches in the S × S office. Likewise, final frames are equivalent to the connector switches in S × S offices. Linefinder frames usually have 10 vertical banks with 40 subscriber terminals on each bank or a capacity of 400 subscribers per linefinder frame. The other selector frames are equipped with 5 vertical banks, each having 100 sets of terminals. Banks are designated 0 to 4, inclusive.

The district, office, incoming, and final frames have a capacity of 60 selectors and 60 *sequence* switches, one for each circuit. Each of the five vertical banks has 100 sets of T, R and S terminals arranged in horizontal rows. These terminals protrude through both sides of the bank. The 60 se-

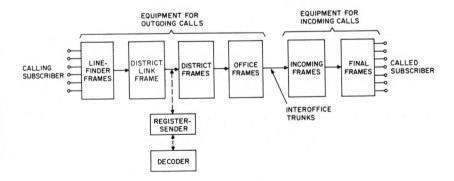

Figure 8-7   Panel System Switching Frames

Figure 8-8   Incoming Frame in Typical Panel Central Office

Shown are power-driven selectors, sequence switches
and relay equipment.

courtesy of AT&T

lectors are divided into 30 on each side of the frame so that every selector
has access to all bank terminals. Each selector is equipped with five brushes,
one for each vertical bank. Therefore, whenever a particular brush is
tripped, contact is made with the respective bank terminals in a similar manner as the wipers on a selector or connector switch in S $\times$ S offices. The selectors on each of these frames are driven by cork rollers, one for updrive
and another for downdrive. The final frame, however, has an additional
updrive roller, rotating about half-speed, to ensure picking the proper terminal during digit selection. These cork rollers are rotated continuously
by electric motors on each frame. A brass commutator and brush assembly are mounted on the top of each selector. As the selector rises during
the selection process, ground or revertive pulses are sent back to the reg-

ister-sender which counts them. When the proper number of pulses have
been received, as determined by the translated data received from the decoder, the register-sender will cause the particular district or office selector to stop at the desired group of bank terminals. The register-sender directs the selections made by the incoming and final circuits from the called
line number that was received by it.

The operation of the selector circuit is controlled by the position of
its related sequence switch. This device is an 18-position rotary switch
which is an integral part of each selector circuit. It is rotated by a constant-
ly revolving vertical drive shaft through an electromechanical clutch under
control of the relays in the circuit. As the sequence switch moves from position to position, various circuit combinations are made or changed. These
combinations control selector operations such as tripping the desired brush,
finding an idle trunk or path, cutting through the talking leads (T and R),
and disconnecting and returning the selector to its normal position upon
completion of the call when the calling party hangs up. See Fig. 8-8.

District and office selectors can have access to almost 500 outgoing
paths or interoffice trunks. Recall that switches in the S $\times$ S system normally have access to only 100 paths. Every local or interoffice trunk terminates in a selector circuit on an incoming frame. The bank terminals of each
incoming frame connect to selector circuits on various final frames. The
vertical banks on the final frames often are split down the center in order
to produce two separate final frames, each with a capacity of 500 line numbers. In this manner, only 10 instead of 20 final frames are needed to serve
a complete 10,000-line panel central office. Figure 8-9 shows the line number relationships between incoming frame bank terminals and final frames.
For example, bank 1 on the incoming frame has access to line numbers between 2000 and 3999. Bank 3 has access to line numbers in the range 6000

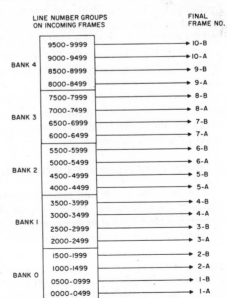

Figure 8-9   Panel Dial System

Illustrated is the relationship of
a line number to a final frame.

to 7999. Therefore, to reach line number 3950, for instance, will necessitate that the selector on the incoming frame be directed by the register-sender to the fourth group (Group 3) on bank 1. This group contains the selectors on final frame No. 4 - B which have access to line numbers 3500 to 3999.

Calls Through Panel Central Office

Referring to Fig. 8 - 10, follow a local call through one of the first types of panel central offices. When the calling party lifts his handset, a linefinder circuit searches for the associated line terminals which, assume, are on bank 4 of the linefinder frame. At the same time, the district-sender link will choose an idle register-sender. Dial tone from the register-sender instructs the subscriber to dial the seven digits of the called number which, suppose, is 241 - 3950. As soon as the first three digits are dialed, the register-sender transmits the office code 241 to a decoder for routing instructions. The decoder returns specific brush and group selections for the district and office selectors to the register-sender and then releases. Assume that the district selector is directed to pick an idle path to an office selector on its bank 3 and group 1. The particular office selector will be lead to bank 1 and group 4 to find an idle trunk to central office 241, which terminates in a selector circuit on an incoming frame in the 241 panel office.

Since the called line number is 3950, the register-sender directs the incoming selector to trip its brush 1 and then to advance to the fourth or top group of terminals on this bank. The bank terminals in this selected group 3 of bank 1 connect to selectors on final frame No. 4 - B which contains line numbers in the sequence 3500 to 3999. Consequently, the register-sender will cause the final selector to trip its 4 brush and then to advance to terminal 50 on bank 4. The final selector, therefore, will be connected to line number 3950. The register-sender, having completed its functions, disconnects and the district circuit advances to cut through the T and R talking leads from the linefinder to the interoffice trunk that had been selected by the office circuit. The incoming frame selector circuit then proceeds to apply ringing to the called line and then talking battery when the called party answers.

If the called line should be busy, the final selector will restore to normal and the final circuit will return a busy-tone. When the calling party hangs up, the district, office, incoming, and final selectors and circuits restore to normal, in that order.

Characteristics of Crossbar Switching System

In both the S $\times$ S and panel systems, selectors establish connections between the calling and called subscribers. These selectors have a wiper or brush assembly that moves over a large number of bank terminals until the desired one is reached. In contrast, the crossbar switch has groups of 10 vertical units, each composed of relay-type contacts. Any one set of contacts is closed by the momentary operation of one of the 10 select magnets, followed by the closure of the hold magnet associated with the particular vertical unit. In the crossbar system there is no brush passing over a sequence of bank terminals; both the type of apparatus and the method of control differ from the S × S and panel systems.

The switches in the S × S systems and the selectors in the panel system are provided with individual control circuits. Separate relay equipment is furnished to enable these selectors to hunt for idle paths or trunks. As a result, considerable apparatus is required in these circuits and is used for relatively few seconds during the establishment of a connection. This equipment is not used again until the call is disconnected and another call set up. In contrast, all of the selecting and trunk-hunting features are incorporated in a few common-control circuits within the No. 5 Crossbar system. This distinctive arrangement greatly speeds up operations because of the relay-like operating characteristics of the crossbar switch. It eliminates the need for substantial amounts of relays and related equipment that otherwise would be required to select outgoing trunks or connect called lines as in the case of the S × S and panel offices.

The subscriber lines appear on both the linefinder and connector switches in S × S offices for handling originating and terminating calls, respectively. Similarly, they connect to both linefinder and final frames in panel offices for the same purpose. In the No. 5 Crossbar system, however, each subscriber line has a single appearance on the line-link frame, which serves for both originating and terminating traffic. The basic switching frames and associated common-control apparatus of a typical No. 5 Crossbar office are shown in Fig. 8-11.

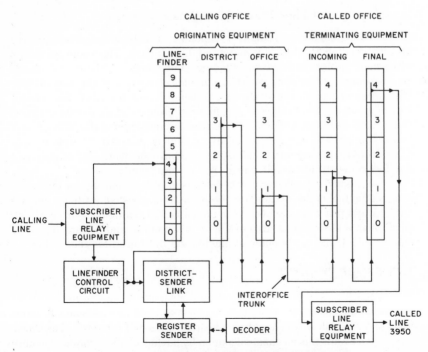

Figure 8-10   Main Equipment of Panel Dial System

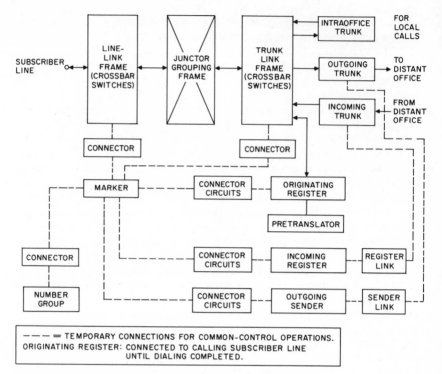

Figure 8-11   No. 5 Crossbar System

Every connection to a calling or called line is established through crossbar switches on the line-link and trunk-link frames. The common-control equipment, which establishes outgoing connections, includes the *marker, connectors, originating register, outgoing sender,* and the *sender link.* For incoming traffic, the common equipment used includes the *marker, incoming register, register link,* the *number group,* and *connector* circuits. Once the connection to the called number is completed and a talking path is established, all common-control equipment is released. Therefore, only the selected crossbar switches on the line-link and trunk-link frames and the designated trunk circuit remain in the connection.

The *junctor grouping* frame is composed of terminal blocks for cross-connecting the paths or junctors between the crossbar switches on the line-link and trunk-link frames. All outgoing and incoming calls are connected through a circuit consisting of a line-link, junctor, and a trunk-link. The marker selects the combination of junctor and links used for each call.

Crossbar Switch

In the S × S and panel systems, the elements of one set of terminals are on a common bank. The other set of terminals are designed to move up in order to make contact with the desired first set of terminals. The crossbar switch avoids this mechanical motion by having a pair of contacts mount-

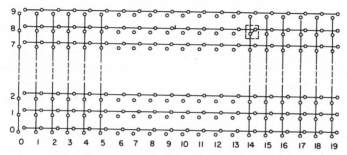

Figure 8-12 Contacts of a Crossbar Switch

Vertical contacts 14 are closed on the 8th horizontal level.

ed at each position in the bank and eliminating the need for contact brushes. In other words, two sets of terminals are mounted in place of the one set used in the S × S and similar switching systems. This arrangement, shown in Fig. 8-12 also eliminates sliding contacts which have greater electrical resistance resulting in noise on the talking paths. Note that the horizontal contacts of each pair on the crossbar switch are multipled with the corresponding contacts of the other pairs in the same vertical row. Therefore, a particular set of contacts may be closed by means of mechanical action analogous to the armature of a relay.

The type of crossbar switch commonly used in the No. 5 Crossbar system has 200 sets of contacts which appear on 10 horizontal and 20 vertical rows of the crossbar switch as illustrated in Fig. 8-12. Figure 8-13 shows the elements of a crossbar switch: the *selecting bar*, *selecting finger*, *actuating spring*, and the *holding bar*. Five selecting bars, one between each horizontal row of contacts, run across the front of the switch and can be rotated a small distance in either direction around its axis by the operation

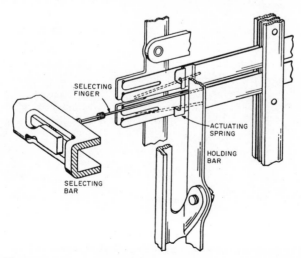

Figure 8-13 Selecting Elements of a Crossbar Switch

of the armatures of two electromagnets. These magnets, called *selecting magnets*, are located at one end of the switch. Wires, called *selecting fingers*, are attached to the selecting bars at each intersection with the vertical columns. These selection fingers project inward towards the contacts and normally rest between the two rows of contacts. When a selecting bar is rotated in one direction, the selecting fingers move up to lie across the backs of the contacts in the row above. When it is rotated in the other direction, the selecting fingers move to extend across the backs of the contacts in the row below. These operations are indicated by the dotted lines in the Fig. 8-13

Each column of contacts has a vertical holding bar which can be rotated by the armature of an electromagnet, called a *holding magnet*, located at the bottom of the crossbar switch. The operation of a holding magnet presses its holding bar against all the selecting fingers in that vertical column. If none of the selecting bars is operated when the holding bar is actuated, the selecting fingers merely will be pushed down between the rows of contacts and no contact will be closed. However, if one of the selecting bars is operated, the selecting fingers of that particular bar will extend across the backs of one row of contacts. With the holding bar in this position, the contacts at this intersection of the selecting and holding bars will be pressed together by the action of the holding bar against the previously rotated selecting finger. Immediately after the holding magnet operates the selecting bar is released and returns to its normal position. The holding bar is held operated by its magnet during the entire period of a call. All selecting fingers, except the one held by the holding bar, restore to their normal position when the selecting bar releases. The selecting bar now is free to be used again with a different holding bar. Figure 8-14 shows a typical crossbar switch. Note that 3 pairs of selecting magnets are on the left side and 2 pairs are on the right side of the switch.

Figure 8-15 illustrates components of a crossbar switch. The typical

Figure 8-14   Typical Crossbar Switch
courtesy of AT&T

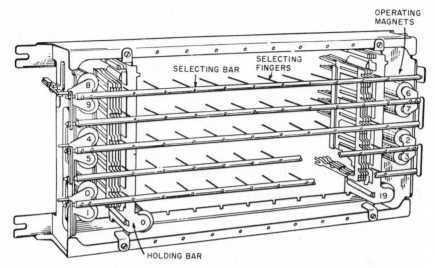

Figure 8-15   Crossbar Switch Components

switch in the No. 5 Crossbar system is composed of 5 pairs of selecting magnets, 20 holding magnets, 5 selecting bars, each with 20 selecting fingers, and 200 sets of crosspoint contacts. Each contact point actually has twin contacts of precious metal to ensure good connections. These contacts are pressed together, as in the operation of a relay, so that very little sliding occurs.

Review Questions

1. Name two principal types of motor-driven common-control switching systems. What is the essential difference between these two systems?
2. What are the main disadvantages of these motor-driven common-control systems?
3. What are the five types of selector frames employed in the panel systems?
4. What are the principal common-control devices used in the motor-driven common-control switching systems?
5. What device controls the operation of all selector circuits in the panel and rotary dial systems?
6. What particular method is used in the panel system to enable the register-sender to control the selections on the various frames?
7. Can common-control operations be incorporated into the step-by-step office? Explain.
8. What is the codelreed? Where is it used?
9. What is the basic switching element in the crossbar system? Describe its main features.
10. What is the main advantage of the contacts used on the crossbar switch as compared to the bank contacts in the S $\times$ S and panel systems?

9

Operations of the No. 5 Crossbar System

Line-Link Frame

Line-link and trunk-link frames are the basic switching frames in the No. 5 Crossbar system; each consist of two bays (groups) of 10 crossbar switches. The bays on the line-link frame are called line and junctor bays while those on the trunk-link frame are called junctor and trunk bays. The horizontal, multiple banks of the 10 crossbar switches on the junctor bay of the line-link frame are cut in half making the equivalent of two crossbar switches of 10 verticals instead of one switch of 20 verticals. One-half (10 verticals) of each switch in the junctor bay is used for junctors or paths between the line-link and trunk-link frames, and the other half of 10 verticals terminates subscriber lines. The terminals on the horizontal banks of the right half of the 10 switches in the junctor bay are wired directly to the corresponding horizontal terminals of the line bay, in effect, providing a crossbar switch of 30 verticals. Subscriber lines are connected to 29 of these verticals of each row of crossbar switches. The remaining vertical is utilized for the "no busy-test" connection. Therefore, each line-link frame can accomodate 290 subscriber lines. These arrangements are shown in Fig. 9-1.

Supplementary bays, having crossbar switches of 10 or 20 verticals, may be added to increase the capacity of the line-link frame, especially for central offices in residential areas. For example, the capacity of a line-link frame may be increased to as many as 590 subscriber lines by adding supplementary bays. Moreover, about 30 classes of subscribers may be served by the same line-link frame. These classes of subscriber services include message rate, flat rate, coin lines, party lines and the various message-rate zones that influence the monthly rates paid. All subscriber lines in the same vertical file of a bay (that is, the corresponding verticals of each

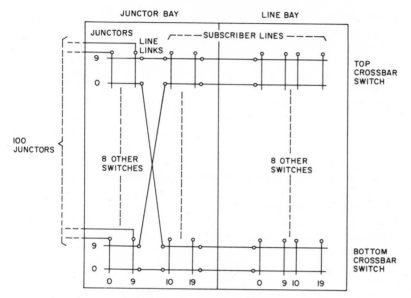

Figure 9-1   Line-Link Frame

Verticals and horizontals of crossbar switches are
designated 0 to 19 and 0 to 9, respectively.

of the 10 crossbar switches of a bay) must be of the same class of service
in order that the class of service is identified for the marker.

The general wiring arrangements of the junctor and line bays of the
line-link frame are indicated in Fig. 9-1 with only the top and bottom crossbar switches of a bay shown. Each crossbar switch is represented by its
top and bottom horizontal crosspoints (0 and 9) and by its first, 10th, 11th
and 20th vertical crosspoints. Note that the horizontals of the junctor bay
switches connect to the horizontals of the line bay switches. Verticals on
the left half of the 10 crossbar switches of the junctor bay connect to junctors. Since each split switch has 10 verticals, there are 100 junctors from
each line-link frame. These 100 junctors, or cross-connection paths, handle all calls to or from subscriber lines on that frame. Each of the 10 horizontals of a line bay crossbar switch connects to a different junctor bay
switch in a regular order. Thus, every line crossbar switch has one link
to each of the 10 junctor crossbar switches, so that every subscriber line
has access to each junctor.

Trunk-Link Frame

In the trunk-link frame, the verticals of the trunk and junctor bays are
interconnected instead of the horizontals, as on the line-link frame. The
crossbar switches of the junctor bay of the trunk-link frame also have their
horizontal multiple cut to provide the equivalent of two crossbar switches of ten verticals each. This split provides terminations for 200 junctors

which connect to the 20 horizontals of each of the 10 junctor crossbar switches. This arrangement is illustrated in Fig. 9-2.

Incoming, outgoing, intraoffice, and other trunks connect to the horizontal crosspoints of the crossbar switches on the trunk bay of the trunk-link frame. Since these are six-point switches, each horizontal crosspoint provides terminations for two trunks—each trunk has a T, R and S lead. The two lower horizontals of each crossbar switch select one or the other of the two trunks associated with each of the upper eight horizontals. Therefore, 16 trunks can terminate on each crossbar switch with a total of 160 on the trunk bay of a trunk-link frame.

All of these 160 terminations however, cannot be used for outgoing trunks. Normally, not more than 120 on a trunk-link frame are used. Likewise, a maximum of 80 terminations can be used for the incoming end of intraoffice trunks. These trunks require two terminations on the trunk-link frame, one for the connection back to the calling subscriber and the other for the connection with the called subscriber. This is necessary since both subscribers are served by the same central office. In addition, five or six terminations usually are provided for connecting calling lines to originating registers as will be explained.

Each trunk-link frame provides 200 junctors and each line-link frame provides only 100 junctors. Therefore, there are normally twice as many line-link frames as trunk-link frames. For example, a typical No. 5 Crossbar office may have 20 line-link and 10 trunk-link frames with each line-link frame having a group of junctors to each trunk-link frame. Hence, 10 junctors, one from each of the 10 crossbar switches of a line-link frame, will connect to each of the 10 trunk-link frames in this particular case. The number of junctors from each line-link frame to each trunk-link frame, however, depends upon the number of trunk-link frames installed. When more than 10 trunk-link frames are required to handle the traffic of an office, each junctor from a line-link will be multipled to two trunk-link frames. This has the effect of doubling the number of junctors from the line-link frames. In this way, each line-link frame can supply a group of 10 junctors to 20 trunk-link frames, which is the maximum capacity of a No. 5 Crossbar central office.

Connectors

Connectors provide paths between the marker and other common-control equipment, and between the marker and the line-link and trunk-link frames. These connecting paths exist for usually less than 0.2 second during the progress of a call.

There are seven different connector designations in the No. 5 Crossbar office. When the particular common-control equipment or crossbar switch frame seizes a marker, the connector is named after that equipment with the word "marker" added. The originating register marker connector, incoming register marker connector, and line-link marker connector are examples of this designation. When the equipment frame is seized by a marker, the word "marker" is omitted from the connector designation. The

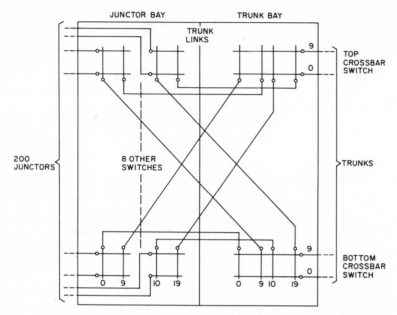

Figure 9-2   Trunk-Link Frames

Only the 1st, 10th, 11th and 20th verticals and the 1st and 10th horizontals of each crossbar switch are shown.

number group connector, outgoing sender connector, trunk-link connector, and the line-link connector are in this category.

Figure 9-3 shows the relationship of the seven connectors with the marker and the various equipment frames. The two different connectors associated with the line-link frame perform different functions. The line-link marker connector signals a marker whenever a subscriber initiates a call. The line-link connector is used by the marker to set up connections between the line-link and trunk-link frames during the progress of a call. Figure 9-3 also indicates the number of paths closed by each connector and the direction of control, that is, whether the connector is seized by the marker or by the particular equipment frame.

A connector is composed of a number of multicontact relays, each of which can close 60 contacts. A multicontact relay has two operating magnets so that it is the equivalent of two 30-contact relays, making it possible to provide the minimum number of relays needed in a particular connector to serve each marker. For example, referring to Fig. 9-3, note that $2\frac{1}{2}$ multicontact relays are required for the number group connector, 2 for the outgoing sender connector, 3 for the trunk-link connector and $1\frac{1}{2}$ for the line-link marker connector. The "$\frac{1}{2}$" relay designation refers to the use of only one of the two operating magnets of a multicontact relay.

There are two types of connectors, single-ended and double-ended, and their use is determined by the wiring of their multicontact relays. See Fig. 9-4 A & B. The double-ended type is used only in the outgoing sender

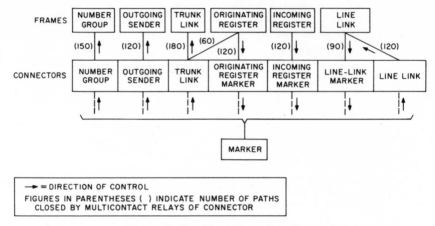

Figure 9-3   No. 5 Crossbar Connectors

connector, the originating register marker connector, and the incoming register marker connector. In the single-ended connector, the armature contacts of the multicontact relays connect directly to the equipment frames served by the connector, requiring one connector for each of the number-group, trunk-link, and line-link frames. The double-ended connector multiple is wired to the armature contacts of two groups of multicontact relays. One group of relays connects to the markers and the other is wired to the several equipment frames served by the connector. Consequently, one double-ended connector can serve a group of similar circuits such as several outgoing senders, originating registers, or incoming registers. Single-ended connectors, however, are used with line-link, trunk-link, and number-group frames because, as soon as these frames are released by one marker, they are free to be seized by another marker. Outgoing senders, originating and incoming registers, on the other hand, are usually not free when disconnected from a marker. The originating register, for example, will be busy recording the digits dialed by a calling subscriber, and the outgoing sender may be transmitting pulses over an outgoing trunk. As a result, double-ended connectors are used with register and sender type of circuits to permit the connector, after it has been released by an originating register or an outgoing sender, to be immediately reused for another connection. If single-ended connectors were used, there would be relatively long intervals when the connector was not in use while the outgoing sender or the originating register were performing their various functions.

The Marker

The operational control of the No. 5 Crossbar switching system is centered in the marker circuit, which establishes all connections within the central office including the paths between crossbar switch frames, idle trunks, and related equipment frames. The marker also determines whether the called line number is idle or busy. The marker may be compared to

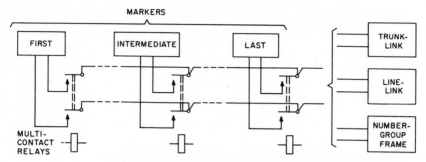

Figure 9-4A   Single-Ended Connector

Any one of the three switch frames chooses an idle marker.
Only one switch frame may operate at any one time.

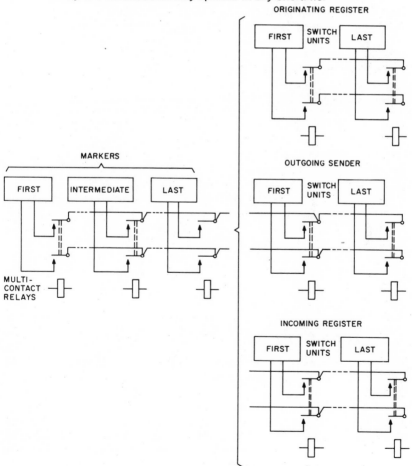

Figure 9-4B   Double-Ended Connector

Any one of the three switch units chooses an idle marker.
Only one switch unit may operate at any one time.

a computer because it receives information, checks its memory for previously programmed instructions, and then initiates an appropriate response by taking certain actions itself or by directing other equipment required to complete a call.

The number of markers installed in a central office generally depends upon the number of subscriber lines and the calling frequency. From three to 12 markers may be provided depending upon the size of the central office and whether business or residential subscribers are served. No. 5 Crossbar offices that serve metropolitan business areas may have as many as 12 markers while suburban offices usually only require three.

Each marker consists of two adjacent equipment frames, each of two bays, that are equipped with relays and associated apparatus. The first frame is composed of the translator and route relays which direct the call-completing functions. The second frame handles the common-control functions including controlling the line, trunk and junctor identification, and selection operations. An additional single bay frame, which is provided to as many as six markers, contains the class-of-service relays and their cross-connection fields. This bay may be equipped with up to 480 route relays in order to afford 40 routes from 20 trunk-link frames to the six markers. Figure 9-5 illustrates the various frames of a marker as well as the equipment frames which are common to a number of markers.

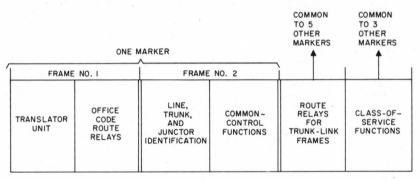

Figure 9-5   Marker Equipment Frames For the No. 5 Crossbar

Dial-Tone Connection by the Marker

As a subscriber lifts the handset of his telephone to place a call, the operations of the marker are initiated. The subscriber line relay (L) on the line-link frame causes the associated line-link marker connector to seize an idle marker. The line-link frame immediately identifies itself to the marker by its frame number and then indicates that a subscriber, on that particular frame, wishes to make a call. The marker then proceeds to establish a dial-tone connection to the calling line. Figure 9-6 illustrates the circuits required for the marker to establish this connection.

After the line-link frame has identified itself to the marker over path 1, the marker searches over testing path 2 for a trunk-link frame not in use by another marker which has an idle originating register connected to it. When the marker finds this idle equipment combination, it immediately seizes it through its associated trunk-link connector, indicated in the diagram by path 3. At this same time an idle originating register is also selected.

Concurrently the marker searches over paths 1 and 4 for the location of the calling subscriber line on the line-link frame. Recall that subscriber lines connect to the verticals of the crossbar switches on the line-link frame. A particular subscriber line, therefore, can be identified by its vertical group, horizontal group, and vertical file locations. A vertical group is composed of the 50 subscriber lines on the corresponding five adjacent verticals of the 10 crossbar switches. These switches are mounted one above the other on the line bay of the line-link frame. There may be from six to 12 vertical groups depending on the number of bays in the line-link frame.

A horizontal group includes the subscriber lines on one horizontal row of crossbar switches on the line-link frame. There are from 29 to 59 subscriber lines in each horizontal group. The designation, vertical file, refers to the 10 subscriber lines that are located vertically above each other on a line-link bay. Accordingly, the identification of the vertical and horizontal groups locate the calling subscriber line as one of five on a particular crossbar switch. Thus the vertical file provides the exact identification of the calling subscriber line out of the five possible lines.

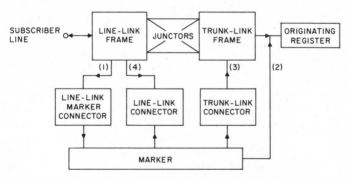

Figure 9-6   Circuits Used By the Marker for Dial-Tone Connection

Refer again to Fig. 9-6 and note that the leads through the line-link marker connector over path 1 transmit to the marker the vertical and horizontal group identification of the calling line. The marker, once the line location is established, connects to that line-link frame via a line-link connector over path 4. It tests the five subscriber lines common to the determined vertical and horizontal groups and selects the calling line. If more than one subscriber should be originating a call in that group, the marker will choose only one in a prescribed order of preference.

These operations have given the marker the locations of the calling line on the line-link frame and an idle originating register on the trunk-link frame. The marker, as a result, will select and close the crosspoints on the crossbar switches by operating the related hold magnets. This results in the connection of the line-link and junctor paths between the calling subscriber line on the line-link frame and the originating register on the trunk-link frame. These paths contain the T, R, and S leads. T and R extend back to the subscriber station and are used for dialing and transmission purposes. The S or sleeve lead is used to hold operated the selected crossbar switches under control of the originating register circuit.

Originating Register Operations

Dial tone is sent to the calling subscriber over the T and R leads from the originating register. Similarly, as in the S × S and panel dial systems, there is an (L) relay in the originating register in series with the subscriber line whose operations are controlled by the subscriber dial. The release and operation of this relay in unison with the dial pulses initiate the counting of these pulses as will be described later. The dial pulses of each digit are counted by a series of counting relays. Each digit requires a group of five relays for storing the number dialed. Therefore, 35 relays would be needed for the usual seven-digit telephone number or 50 relays for a 10-digit call including the area code. At the end of each digit, the recorded number is transferred to the digit registering circuit of the originating register. The counting relays then are released so that they can be used to count the pulses of the next digit.

The pulse counting method, illustrated by Fig. 9-7, shows relays (LC), (LD), (LE), (RA), (RA1), and the (P1) to (P6) relays which perform the pulse counting functions. Relay (L) is held operated over the subscriber line loop, and operates (LA) and (SR). The (SR) relay (slow-release type) remains operated when (L) releases momentarily during dialing.

Each dial pulse causes relays (L) and (LA) to release and then reoperate. The first release of (L) operates (LC). The reoperation of (L) makes (LE) operate in series with (LC). The second release of (L) operates (LD) and also holds operated relay (LE). The operation of relay (LD) releases (LC). When relay (L) reoperates at the end of the second pulse, (LD) and (LE) release. The third dial pulse produces the same action as the first pulse, and the fourth pulse causes the same process as the second. In effect, the (LE) relay is operated by each odd pulse and released by each even pulse.

Referring to Fig. 9-7, note that counting relays (P1) to (P6) are controlled by the operation and release of (LE). For example, the first operation of (LE) operates relay (P1). The first release of (LE) operates relay (P2) which releases relay (P1). The next operation of (LE) operates relay (P3) which, in turn, releases relay (P2). This sequence continues until all pulses for the digit are completed, at which time relay (RA) releases because (L) remains operated for a longer time (more than 0.2 second) while the subscriber starts to dial the next digit. The release of relay (RA) connects ground through the contacts of the various operated counting relays, (P1) through (P6), in order to record the number of the dialed digit in the digit registering circuit. This is accomplished by a ground on two out of the five leads to the digit registering circuit in accordance with the code in Fig. 9-8. If the first digit dialed was 8, relays (P2) and (P6) in the counting relay chain would

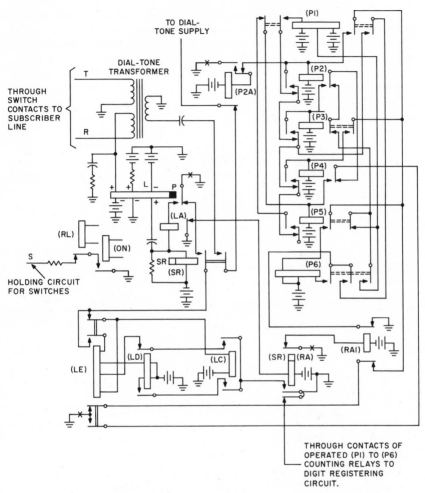

Figure 9-7   Dial-Pulse Counting Circuit in Originating Register

be operated to ground leads 1 and 7 to the digit registering circuit. And if 6 was the second digit dialed, counting relays (P5) and (P6) would be operated to ground leads 2 and 4 to the digit registering circuit.

The release of (RA) at the end of the digit dialed also operates the (RA1) relay which releases relays (LC) and (LE) if they should be operated. In addition, (RA1) releases all operated (P1) to (P6) counting relays so that they may be used to count the pulses of the next digit dialed.

As soon as all seven digits have been recorded, the originating register calls for a marker and then transmits this information to it. In the smaller offices, such as those serving suburban areas, the same type of marker is used for providing dial-tone connections and completing calls. Separate markers, however, are used in the larger offices in cities because of the greater volume of traffic. The marker used for completing calls usually is termed the *completing marker*.

The completing marker or marker selects an idle intraoffice trunk on the trunk-link frame and determines the crossbar switches on the line-link and trunk-link frames that should be used to connect the calling subscriber to the intraoffice trunk. Upon completion of this selection, the marker signals the originating register to release its connection to the calling subscriber line. However, the connection between the marker and the originating register is maintained so that the information recorded in the latter will be available until the marker completes its functions. The subscriber line-to-originating register connection is released before the subscriber line-to-intraoffice trunk connection is established because the trunk-link frame is used for both connections.

Dial Pulse Counting Code

No. of Dial Pulses	Relays Operated	Leads Grounded	No. of Dial Pulses	Relays Operated	Leads Grounded
1	(P1)	0 and 1	6	(P5), (P6)	2 and 4
2	(P2)	0 and 2	7	(P1), (P6)	0 and 7
3	(P3)	1 and 2	8	(P2), (P6)	1 and 7
4	(P4)	0 and 4	9	(P3), (P6)	2 and 7
5	(P5)	1 and 4	10	(P4), (P6)	4 and 7

Figure 9-8

When the subscriber-to-intraoffice trunk connection is made, the circuit between the originating register and the marker is released. Both circuits, consequently, restore to normal to become available for other calls. The originating register is employed for about 15 to 20 seconds, depending on the time required by the subscriber to dial the called number. The marker, however, requires only a fraction of a second to function as determined by the time needed to test and select an idle trunk and connecting link, and to actuate the magnets of the selected crossbar switches.

Number Group Frame

Since an intraoffice call (call to another subscriber in the same No. 5 Crossbar office) is being traced, a sender is not required. The marker, at the same time that it selects an idle intraoffice trunk, connects to the required number group frame through a number group connector. The number group frame is a sort of central file which maintains the assignment list of the crossbar switch locations on the different line-link frames for the corresponding directory numbers. The marker, in effect, asks the number group frame, "On which line-link frame and where on that frame will the line corresponding to the called number be found?" At the same time this information is sent from the number group frame to the marker, it will also inform the marker about the type of ringing or ringing combination required for the called number.

A total of 1000 consecutive directory numbers may be served by one number group frame. Ten number group frames, therefore, would be needed to serve a full 10,000-line office. The first number group frame serves numbers in the series 0000 - 0999, the second frame serves numbers 1000 - 1999, etc., up to frame 10 for numbers 9000 - 9999. The upper half of the number-group frame is equipped with relays which receive the called number from the marker. These relays extend the various leads from the marker to three cross-connecting fields of terminal blocks which occupy the lower half of the frame. See Fig. 9 - 9.

The actual translation of the number into the corresponding equipment locations on the line-link frame is accomplished by jumpers or cross-connection wires placed between the terminal blocks on these three fields. The bottom field, designated LL, identifies the number of the line-link frame. The center or RF field serves to identify the vertical file and the ringing combination and VHG, the top field, indicates the particular vertical and horizontal group locations on the indicated crossbar switch.

Each cross-connection field is composed of an array of 1000 terminals in numerical sequence, representing the directory numbers assigned to that number group frame, and another arrangement of terminals for the specific crossbar switch locations or ringing combinations. Translation

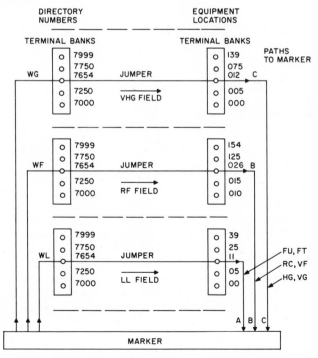

Figure 9 - 9   Cross-Connection Fields on Number-Group Frame

is accomplished by connecting a jumper from a specific directory number terminal to the terminal associated with its equipment location, or to the required ringing-combination terminal. For example, assume that the called line number is 7654. The selection of the number group frame is dictated by the thousands digit of the called number. Therefore, the marker will connect to number group frame 7 and will be concerned only with the translation of number 654 within that frame.

Figure 9-9 shows how the translation of this number is effected by the cross-connections on the three fields of number group frame 7. In the LL field, terminal 654 is connected to line-link frame 11 through terminal LL-11. In the RF field, connection is made to terminal 026 corresponding to ringing combination 2 and vertical file 6. The VHG field's cross-connection to terminal 012 corresponds to vertical group 1 and horizontal group 2 on line-link frame 11.

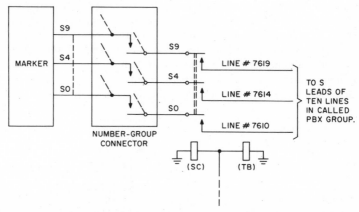

Figure 9-10   Simplified Circuit for Testing for Idle PBX Lines by Marker

The translation process proceeds as follows. When the marker connects to number group frame 7, it places a d-c potential on number 654 (directory number 7654) and on each of paths WL, WF and WG as shown in the figure. The cross-connecting wires extend this potential, in turn, to the terminals of the particular equipment location; in this case, LL-11, RF-026 and VHG-012, respectively. These d-c potentials then are returned to the marker over the three specific paths indicated in the figure. The tens and units digits of the line-link frame FT, FU are sent over path A. The ringing combination and vertical file RC, VF data are sent over path B, and the horizontal and vertical group numbers HG, VG are transmitted over path C. In this manner, the called party's equipment location and ringing combination will be translated for use by the marker so that it now can proceed to complete the call.

Another important function is performed for the marker by the number group frame with respect to PBX lines. In S × S, panel and similar type dial systems, PBX lines (Private Branch Exchange, installed on a customer's premises and served by several lines from the central office) must have a consecutive sequence of directory numbers. For instance, 7610, 7611, 7612, 7613 and 7614. This arrangement is necessary so that the S × S connector or the final selector in the panel office can continue to hunt for an idle line in the particular PBX group in case its first or next several lines are busy.

In the No. 5 Crossbar system, however, it is not necessary that all PBX lines have consecutive directory numbers as long as they are in the same number group frame. The called number given to the marker normally will be that of the first line of the desired PBX group. First the ringing combination 10 is cross-connected to all PBX lines numbers in the RF field. Then, an (SC) relay is provided for testing the S or busy-test leads of up to 10 lines in the particular PBX group. This is accomplished by extending these S leads to the number group connector as illustrated in Fig. 9-10. Ten additional leads are also provided between the number group connector and the marker over which these S leads may be tested by the latter.

Thus, when the marker receives ringing combination code 10 from the number group frame, it initiates a test of the 10 S leads of the desired PBX group. If an idle line is found, the marker sends a units code to the number group frame for translation into that line's location on the line-link frame. Where there are more than 10 lines in the called PBX group, additional (SC) relays will be associated with all of the (TB) relays that have lines of that PBX group. In addition, circuit provisions are made for advancing from one (SC) relay to another if all the PBX lines associated with the particular (SC) relay should be busy.

Completing Calls with the Marker

Figure 9-11 illustrates the circuits which the marker must use to complete a call. The number group frame transmits over path 1 the called line numerical combination and location on a particular line-link frame. Once the marker has this information, it seizes the appropriate line-link frame over path 2, and then tests the S lead of the called line to check if it is idle or busy by the same method as was described for PBX lines. Assuming that the called line is idle, the marker over paths 2 and 3 select an idle link and junctor circuit between the called line location on its line-link frame and the previously selected intraoffice trunk on the trunk-link frame. At the same time, the marker will again connect to the line-link frame of the calling line over path 4 in order to find an idle connection from the calling line to the other end of the intraoffice trunk.

Before releasing, the marker passes the ringing information to the intraoffice trunk over path 3 and the intraoffice trunk applies ringing current to the called line. When the party answers, the intraoffice trunk supervises the call, supplies the talking battery, and holds operated the holding magnets of the operated crosspoints on the line-link and trunk-link crossbar switches during the call. When the calling party disconnects, the intraoffice trunk will release these holding magnets. If the called party disconnects first, nothing happens for a period of about 15 to 30 seconds at which time an

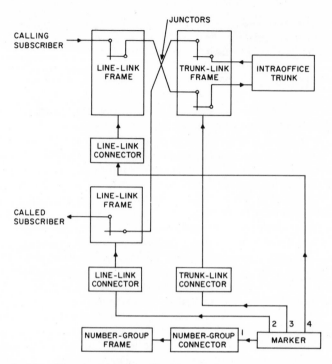

Figure 9-11   Circuits Used by Marker for Completing Intraoffice Call

alarm circuit will function to release the trunk circuit. If the called line should test busy, the marker will instruct the intraoffice trunk circuit to return a busy signal to the calling subscriber.

A sender, with its associated sender connector and sender link, is used on all outgoing calls except intraoffice and calls to the operator. Figure 9-12 indicates how the marker handles outgoing calls in association with the sender and its affiliated circuits. In this example, the marker, upon receiving the called number from the originating register over path 1, recognizes from the office code that the call is for a subscriber in a distant central office. The marker, accordingly, finds and seizes an idle sender through a sender connector circuit over path 2. Next, the marker transmits to the sender all digits of the called number that had been received from the originating register. Since this is an interoffice call, the marker directs the sender to prepare to transmit only the last four digits which correspond to the called line number.

At the same time the marker is transmitting the called number to the sender, it is seeking an idle trunk-link frame over path 3 which must also have an idle trunk to the desired distant office. Upon finding a desired idle trunk over path 5, the marker over path 3 connects the sender to the selected trunk via the sender link frame. This is accomplished by having the trunks and senders appear on crossbar switches of a sender link frame. Each frame has a maximum of 10 crossbar switches with trunks connected to their verticals and senders to their horizontal crosspoints. The trunks assigned to one crossbar switch are associated with the same trunk-link frame. The senders are arranged in groups depending upon their type of pulsing. All senders of a group are multipled to all crossbar switches of the sender link frames that have trunks requiring that type of sender. Furthermore, the horizontal level to which the sender is connected on the sender link frame was sent to the marker when it first seized the sender. Consequently, the marker is able to connect the outgoing trunk to the proper sender.

Next, the marker seizes the line-link frame of the calling subscriber over path 4. The originating register has already informed the marker of the particular line-link frame number and the location of the calling line on it. With this information, the marker now proceeds over paths 3 and 4 to select and connect a junctor circuit between the calling subscriber line on the line-link frame and the input to the selected outgoing, interoffice trunk on the trunk-link frame. With the completion of this path, the marker signals the sender that it can pulse out the digits for the called number to the distant office equipment, and the marker releases.

The sender records each digit received from the marker on a set of five relays. Only two of these five relays in each set are used to record any one digit. The five relays are designated 0, 1, 2, 4 and 7. The sum of the two operated relays indicate the particular digit except that relays 4 and 7 are operated for digit 0. Figure 9-13 lists the relay code used. It is a 2-out-of-5 recording method which provides a check on improper operations because an error will be indicated if fewer or more than two relays are operated. In addition to this information the sender also receives from the marker information pertaining to the class of call, any special handling instructions and initial entry data for the Central Automatic Message Accounting (CAMA) circuits where this feature is provided.

The main function of the sender is to transmit the called number to

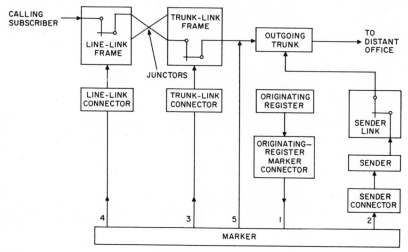

Figure 9-12   Circuits Used by Marker for Calling Another Central Office

the switching equipment in the distant office. Three principal kinds of senders are used for this function depending upon the type of switching apparatus installed in the called office. They are designated multifrequency (MF), dial-pulse, and revertive-pulse senders.

Multifrequency (MF) senders offer the fastest transmission of the called number, usually at the rate of above seven digits per second. This type of signaling employs two separate tones in the 700-to-1700-Hz range. They are sent simultaneously for each digit, as explained in Chapter 4. This type of sender can only be utilized if the called office is equipped for receiving MF pulses. Crossbar offices, such as the No. 1, No. 5, crossbar toll, and crossbar tandem offices, normally are so equipped.

Dial-pulse senders transmit the called number in the form of dial pulses for each digit. The transmission speed is relatively slow, usually about one digit per second. This sender is employed primarily for completing calls to S $\times$ S offices but may be used for transmitting the called number to No. 5 Crossbar, crossbar toll and crossbar tandem offices.

Revertive-pulse senders are used on calls to panel offices. This particular type of sender controls the operations of the selectors in the incoming and final frames of the panel office. It functions in a similar manner as the register sender.

Outgoing Sender Digit-Recording Code

Digit	Relays Operated	Digit	Relays Operated
0	4 and 7	5	1 and 4
1	0 and 1	6	2 and 4
2	0 and 2	7	0 and 7
3	1 and 2	8	1 and 7
4	0 and 4	9	2 and 7

Figure 9-13

On a normal call, only a few seconds are needed for the outgoing sender to complete its work. Accordingly, only about 10 MF and 10 dial-pulse senders may be adequate to handle the outgoing traffic of a 10,000-line, No. 5 Crossbar central office. To prevent a sender from being held for a long period in case a trouble condition is encountered, a timing circuit is provided. If the call is not completed within a prescribed interval, the timing circuit releases the sender. The timing circuit will also send a reorder or overflow tone signal to the calling party as an indication to hang up and make the call again.

Termination of Incoming Calls

Before the outgoing sender in the calling office can transmit the called number to the distant No. 5 Crossbar office, this office must complete a number of preparatory steps. Outgoing trunk circuits in calling offices terminate on incoming trunk circuits in the called office. These incoming trunks

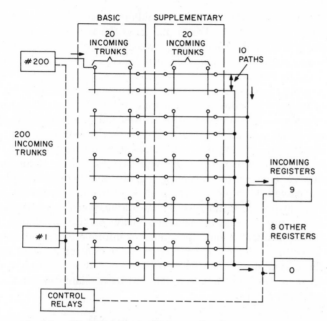

Figure 9-14   Arrangement of Incoming-Register Link Frames

appear on both the trunk-link and incoming register link frames. The incoming register link frame provides access to a particular group of incoming registers, depending upon the category of the calling central office. For example, MF incoming registers normally are used for incoming calls from other No. 5 Crossbar offices, dial-pulse incoming registers for calls from S × S offices, and revertive-pulse type incoming registers for incoming calls from panel offices.

Each incoming register link frame has five crossbar switches of the 20-vertical type together with their control relays. The incoming trunks are connected to the verticals of this crossbar switch and the incoming registers are wired to its horizontals. Therefore, 100 incoming trunks, one per a vertical of each of the five crossbar switches, can have direct access to a group of 10 incoming registers. This results because each incoming register is multipled to one horizontal level on each of the five crossbar switches on the incoming register link frame. Depending upon traffic load requirements, a supplementary frame containing five similar crossbar switches may be added to increase to 200 the number of incoming trunks having access to the same ten incoming registers. This arrangement is illustrated in Fig. 9-14. Upon seizing an idle incoming register, the incoming register link circuit transmits the frame number and the class of incoming trunk involved. The frame number is that of the trunk-link frame on which the particular incoming trunk appears. This data is used later by the marker for connecting the trunk to the called line number. The class of trunk indicates information such as the number of digits to be received, whether the trunk is arranged for local, tandem or toll service, or other special instructions. In the case of tandem and toll trunks, a number group location also is sent for subsequent use by the marker in obtaining the line-link frame location of a tandem or toll trunk. Such trunks appear on both the trunk-link and line-link frames when a No. 5 Crossbar office serves as a tandem or toll connecting switching center.

The succeeding steps concerned in terminating an incoming call from a distant office may be followed by referring to Fig. 9-15. After the incoming register records the information, it causes the incoming trunk circuit to signal the outgoing sender in the calling office to pulse out the called number. The MF pulses from the Outgoing sender are received and stored by the incoming register using sets of five relays as described for the outgoing sender. As soon as the incoming register is satisfied that all digits have been received, it requests over path 1 an incoming register marker connector circuit which, in turn, seizes an idle marker over path 2. Next, the incoming register transmits, simultaneously to the marker over paths 1 and 2, the called number and other items of information it had received. Since the incoming register is connected to the marker by a larger number of wires, the essential data can be sent within a few milliseconds, allowing the marker to quickly complete a call and be available to handle thousands of calls per hour.

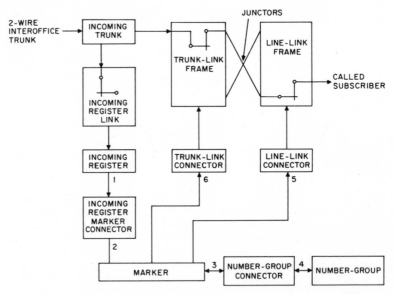

Figure 9-15   Circuits Used for Completing Incoming Call

Assume that the information received by the marker indicates that the particular incoming trunk is of the interoffice type and is located on trunk-link frame 6, that the called number is 4321, and that there are no special instructions for completing the call. The marker completes this interoffice incoming call in exactly the same manner as for an intraoffice call. It first connects to number group frame 4 over paths 3 and 4 in order to obtain the specific line-link frame and location of the called line number on it. With this information, the marker seizes the indicated line-link frame over path 5 and tests the called line. If it is idle, the marker, through paths 5 and 6, immediately selects an idle link and junctor circuit to connect the called line location on its line-link frame with the incoming trunk on the trunk-link frame, and then releases. Subsequent operations are the same as were described for completing an intraoffice type of call.

Incoming calls from S $\times$ S and panel central offices are completed in the same manner. Different types of incoming registers are employed, as explained, to receive the called numbers and to translate the recorded data into the proper form for transmission to the marker. Various other types of calls can be controlled by the No. 5 Crossbar system but the foregoing descriptions of handling intraoffice and interoffice calls present the fundamentals of this modern, common-control, electromechanical switching system.

Review Questions

1. What are the basic switching frames in the No. 5 Crossbar system? How many subscriber lines can be accomodated by one frame?
2. What is the name of the connecting paths between the basic switching frames? How many connecting paths are normally provided by each frame?
3. What functions are performed by the connectors? Name at least three different connector circuits.
4. What main functions are performed by the marker?
5. What switching frame and equipment units are used by the marker in establishing a dial-tone connection?
6. How are the subscriber dial-pulses recorded?
7. What is the purpose of the number group frame? How many lines does it serve?
8. What additional equipments are used for handling an interoffice call that are not required for an intraoffice call?
9. What relays in the outgoing sender are operated for recording the digits of the called number 1920?
10. What additional equipment is provided for completing incoming calls from a distant crossbar central office?

10

Electronic Switching Systems

Need for Electronic Switching

In the foregoing chapters, two basic types of automatic electromechanical switching systems have been studied: *direct control*, in which the subscriber dial directly controls the equipment which establishes a connection, and *common-control* in which the switching equipment completes calls through the shared use of a small quantity of sophisticated equipment.

The direct control system is typified by the step-by-step (S $\times$ S) central office. Currently it serves nearly all of the lines of the Independent Telephone companies in the United States and about 44 percent of the Bell System's lines.

Common-control systems serve the remaining 55 percent of the Bell System's lines and can be divided between 48 percent crossbar and 7 percent panel dial systems.

At the present time electronic switching systems (ESS) serve only 1 percent of the telephones in use but it may be anticipated that almost every central office will be equipped with electronic equipment by the year 2000. The capabilities of electromechanical direct and common-control equipment to handle the increasing volume of traffic and provide for the expanding service features are severely limited by the slow switching speeds of these systems. As a result, research and development efforts have been directed for many years towards producing a workable and economical electronic switching system. The recent development of solid-state devices, such as transistors and integrated circuits, have greatly increased switching speeds, leading to the development of electronic switching.

Essentially it is speed that justifies the need for greater complexity of an electronic switching system. For example, it is now possible to switch, or change circuit conditions at speeds of a few *nanoseconds*, one billionth of a second (10^{-9} seconds). Several milliseconds are usually required for switching—relay operations—in the electromechanical system. The higher speeds of the electronic devices make it possible for a single common-control element in an electronic switching office to serve as many as 65,000 lines. The No. 5 Crossbar office, on the other hand, is normally capable of serving only 10,000 lines and it requires a number of duplicate groups of control equipment.

Electronic Switching Concepts

The electronic switching systems that have been developed differ materially from the electromechanical systems. Instead of merely replacing relays, selectors, and crossbar switches of the electromechanical systems with transistors or other electronic circuitry many new concepts have been evolved. Two principal types of electronic systems, constructed and placed in service, employ a different control and transmission approach although both use similar techniques. They are designated the time division multiplex (TDM) and the space division categories.

The TDM electronic switching system may be pictured as comprising a common highway over which all conversations take place. This highway is time-shared by all connecting subscriber lines and trunks through a series of high speed electronic gates. Initial developments by the Automatic Electric Company and the Bell Telephone Laboratories utilized this method. The Automatic Electric Company's EAX and the Bell System's No. 101 ESS employed TDM means of electronic switching. This particular type is more suitable for PBX installations and small central offices although recent improvements have increased the capacity of the No. 101 ESS to 3000 lines. The space division method establishes an individual path between the calling and called lines which is the basis of the Bell System's No. 1 ESS.

TDM uses a common transmission path or highway which may be compared to the frequency division method of telephone carrier systems whereby several voice channels are stacked on the same conductors. A different frequency band is used for each voice channel in this type of carrier system. In the TDM system, on the other hand, a speech signal is sampled on a repetitive basis and transmitted in a definite time sequence with respect to the samples of the other voice channels. This method, which also is utilized in the pulse code modulation (PCM) carrier system, is illustrated in Fig. 10-1.

In order to faithfully transmit and reproduce the original voice signals, they must be sampled instantaneously at regular intervals and at a rate which is at least twice the highest significant frequency of the signal. Because voice channels normally cover a 200-3200-Hz range or a nominal 4000-Hz bandwidth, a sampling rate of 8000 Hz is generally employed in order that two samples can be taken during each half-cycle of the speech signal. These samples are then transmitted as a series of pulses over the common transmission path. In this manner, the same transmission facility may be time-shared by many calls.

Referring to Fig. 10-1, follow a call in a TDM electronic switching office where subscriber A is talking to subscriber B which the control and

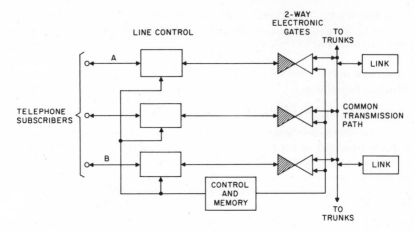

Figure 10-1   Basic Elements of TDM Electronic Switching System

memory circuits remember. Line A is connected to the common highway in its assigned time slot. At the same time, an idle link also is connected to the highway and a sample from A is transmitted into it and temporarily stored. When the time slot of line B is connected to the highway by its electronic gate, the link will also be connected. Thus, the sample stored in the link will be transmitted to B during this slot period. This same process occurs on a two-way basis from B to A. The control and memory circuits are required to remember that subscribers A and B are talking to each other, and to send appropriate controlling pulses to the electronic gates at the proper intervals.

The transmission paths of the TDM electronic switching system generally follow the concepts of the space division type. This chapter will concentrate primarily on the principles, techniques, and equipment that have been designed for the Bell System's No. 1 ESS electronic switching system. It should be understood, however, that they also are applicable in many respects to other electronic switching systems such as the EAX type of Automatic Electric Company. The new electronic switching systems, which eventually will replace the electromechanical types, make use of the stored program incorporating *logic, memory,* and a *central control* unit to govern operations. The No. 1 ESS is composed of two main parts designated the *central control* and the *switching network;* each part functions separately.

The central control unit has the following five principal elements associated with it: 1 *line scanner,* 2 *program store,* 3 *call store.* 4 the *switching network,* and 5 *administration and maintenance center.* These elements and their location are shown in Fig. 10-2. Note that there is a continuing bilateral exchange of information between central control and its related components. This interchange mainly concerns the status of subscriber lines and calls in progress. The teleprinter is the communication device used between central control and the administrative and maintenance personnel.

Many new nomenclatures, as would be expected, are linked with electronic switching techniques which have no counterpart in electromechanical systems. A number of them relate to computer and data processing procedures. For instance, *memory* and *logic* play important roles in all switching systems; *memory* contains the stored instructions, while *logic* makes the decisions on how to use the instructions. Recall that in the No. 5 Crossbar system the originating register provides the memory and the marker makes the logical decisions.

A memory provides a storage space for data and instructions: it stores the program of instructions as well as the data words upon which the instructions operate. Information may be programmed into the memory and extracted from it; therefore the information stored in the memory of the No. 1 ESS may be temporary or semipermanent. Temporary storage of memory may be regarded as an electronic slate. For example, the call store unit is a temporary memory that records the instantaneous state of a subscriber line, registers the digits dialed and notes other transitory data during the progress of a call. When the call is completed, this electronic memory slate is wiped clean of the information.

Any material or device that possesses at least two stable states has a memory. The ordinary light switch is an everyday example of a memory device because it has two stable states, on and off, and it "remembers" its position as the result of a manual operation. Relays also can remember an electrical command; they have functioned as memory devices in electromechanical offices for many years. Their operating and release speeds, however, are too slow for general use in electronic switching systems. The memory devices developed for the No. 1 ESS may be classified as the permanent magnet *twistor* type used for semipermanent storage in the program store, and the *ferrite sheet* mechanism for temporary storage purposes in the call store unit.

An additional departure from electromechanical switching systems

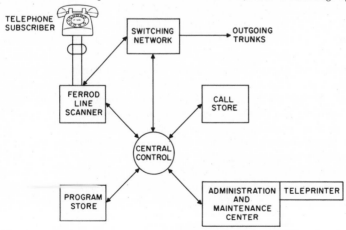

**Figure 10-2   Principal Elements of No. 1 ESS
Electronic Switching System**

Figure 10-3   Ferrod Sensor
courtesy of Bell Telephone Laboratories

is the omission of the (L) and cutoff (CO) relays from all subscriber lines. Instead, each subscriber line connects to a saturable-core transformer called a *ferrod sensor*. This device, show in Fig. 10-3, indicates whether the line is on-hook or off-hook. Each *ferrod sensor* is scanned about five times every second by electronic circuits in the No. 1 ESS to determine if a change of state has occurred; that is, from on-hook to off-hook or vice-versa.

Another essential device is the *ferreed* crosspoint switch, Fig. 10-4, which performs the switching operations in the line-link and trunk-link networks. It may be compared to the crossbar switch. The ferreed consists of two magnetic reeds sealed in a glass envelope mounted between plates of a two-state magnetic alloy. This alloy can be switched very quickly from one state to another with very short pulses of current. It remains magnetically saturated until another current pulse switches the alloy back to the original state. The *ferreed* also may be compared to the codelreed type of relay that was described in Ch. 8, except that it operates in fractions of a millisecond. The ferreed crosspoints only switch the T and R of the talking paths. The selection of idle paths and trunks is accomplished by other electronic means.

Electronic Gates and Logic Circuits

Basically, the memory devices in the No. 1 ESS store the binary digits or *bits* in a memory cell and recall them on command. Millions of bits may be recalled after only a few microseconds while others may be stored for years and recalled repeatedly as often as required.

The binary system is based on the powers of 2 in contrast to the decimal system which is based on the powers of 10. A bit (an abbreviation for binary digit) represents one of two conditions or states. In electronic switching systems, the binary digit 1 can represent the presence of a signal, or a true or yes condition. The 0 binary digit can indicate the absence of a signal, or a false or no condition.

Digits in the decimal system may be converted to binary form by the use of code groups of binary bits to represent each of the ten decimal digits. A four-bit binary code, used in the EAX system for this purpose, is shown in Fig. 10-5. Each bit in this table has a value or weight. The bit at the extreme left has a weight of 1 and the bit at the extreme right has a weight of 8. The decimal digit represented by the code group is obtained by adding the weights of the positions in which a binary 1 appears. For example, the decimal digit 6 is composed of binary bits 0110 in that order. By adding the weights of the positions in which 1 appears, 2 + 4, one obtains a total of 6.

Logic circuits are very important elements of electronic switching systems. Electronic gates, mentioned in connection with TDM electronic switching systems, are specimens of logic circuits. In reality, the electronic gate

Figure 10-4   Ferreed Switch
courtesy of AT&T

or gating circuit is a relatively simple electronic switching circuit employing solid-state devices, such as transistors and diodes. It allows information, which may be in the form of electrical pulses, to flow through if certain signals are present. If other than the desired signals are present, it
will prevent the flow of the information.

The transistor generally is used as the gating or switching device in
logic circuits because it is capable of providing current, voltage, or power
gain to drive succeeding circuits. In addition, the transistor can invert the
input signal and can match output to input impedance for optimum power
transfer.

4-Bit Binary Code

Decimal Digit	Code-Weights			
	1	2	4	8
0	0	1	0	1
1	1	0	0	0
2	0	1	0	0
3	1	1	0	0
4	0	0	1	0
5	1	0	1	0
6	0	1	1	0
7	1	1	1	0
8	0	0	0	1
9	1	0	0	1

Figure 10-5

These logic or gating circuits furnish certain logical relations which, by
convention, have been classified as AND, OR and NOT gates. For instance,
in the AND gate, electrical pulses appearing simultaneously on all its input
leads would produce a pulse on the output lead. However, if the pulses
do not appear simultaneously on all the input leads, no pulse will be present on the output lead. Another and more commonplace example is a read-
ing lamp plugged into a wall socket which is controlled by a wall switch.
The lamp will not light unless both the lamp switch AND the wall switch
are turned on.

The OR gate is a multiple-input circuit having an output that can be
energized only when one or more of any of the input circuits are in a specified state. A simple illustration of the OR logical function is the action of the
interior lights of an automobile. They will light only if one front door OR
another door is opened.

The NOT gate actually is a simple input circuit whose output is energized only if its input is not energized. This type of gate circuit is also an
inverting amplifier. For example, when its input is grounded a negative
potential will appear on the output lead. Similarly, when a negative voltage is applied to the input of the NOT gate, approximately zero voltage will
be present at its output. The corresponding logic operations and logical
symbols of these gates are illustrated in Fig. 10-6 in addition to the AND,

OR and NOT logic operations represented by the indicated mathematical signs.

The input and output levels of these logic elements may be referred to by the binary digits 1 or 0 instead of in terms of voltage. A binary 1 can be regarded as representing a negative potential and 0 as being zero volts or ground potential. In this manner, two or more input leads of an AND gate, for example, can be compared to give a 1 (true or yes) conclusion or a 0 (false or no) result on the output lead.

The AND, OR, and NOT gates comprise three of the basic logic elements used for electronic switching functions. The switching roles of these gates depend upon adequate signal levels so that amplifiers usually are included in these circuits. Time is another very important element. Its importance necessitates the use of storage devices. Thus, in summary, we can state that the basic logic elements are composed of switching, amplification, and storage devices, all of which are essential components of the No. 1 ESS and EAX electronic switching systems.

Stored Program Functions

The use of a stored program system to control operations contributes great flexibility to the No. 1 ESS since the stored program system offers a changeable memory and logic. A measure of the flexibility that is possible by this means can be realized by comparing the logic methods employed in the electromechanical system.

In electromechanical systems, the connecting copper wires "contained" the logic and each circuit was wired to perform a specific programmed operation. As a result it usually was necessary to add or replace equipment and to rewire circuits in order to effect a change in operations. Moreover, it often would cost more to modify the existing equipment for new features than to provide these features with a new system. In contrast, the stored

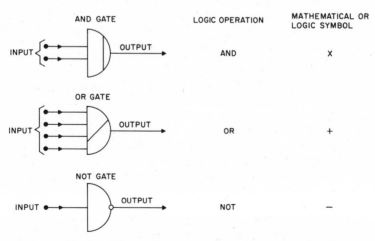

Figure 10-6   Gating Circuits and Associated Logic Symbols

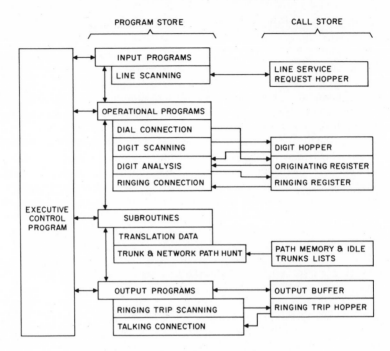

Figure 10-7   Stored Program Components

program in the No. 1 ESS is contained on plug-in cards which are inserted in the memory. Consequently, it only is necessary to change a memory card to alter a logical operation in the stored program. This facility enables future design concepts or additional services to be readily added to existing No. 1 ESS offices.

In the electromechanical system, each operation in the switching sequence triggers the operation that follows it. In the No. 1 ESS, the *program store* is the trigger. For instance, it may initially direct that dial tone be sent to a subscriber originating a call, next a connection could be made to the *switching network* for another call followed by the release of the connections for a third call and, only then, to return to the first call to record the dialed digits. Any one step in processing a single call is segregated from any other step. From the subscriber's viewpoint, the call appears to continue in an unbroken sequence until the connection is completed. Only one call at a time may be handled by the system but its enormous operating speed makes it seem as though all calls are being handled simultaneously.

The actual circuit actions that accomplish each step in the process take place in *central control* as directed by the program store. Every few microseconds one of the approximate 100,000 instruction words in the stored program directs central control in some basic operation of call processing or automatic maintenance. While each step may have a different duration, the flow of actions follows an exact schedule since only one instruction at a time can be executed by central control. For example, the condition of each subscriber line normally is scanned once every 200 milliseconds. However, during dialing the line must be scanned at a faster rate to avoid missing any digit pulses. The *switching network* operates at a slower rate so that instructions to make connections in it are issued at correspondingly slower rates. These different time cycles are reflected in the formation of the stored program. Some of the essential components of the program store and the call store, which comprise the memory and logic of the No. 1 ESS, are outlined in Fig. 10-7. The stored program contains five functional groups of programmed logic. Each controls a particular phase in handling a call. The following is a brief description of the functions of each group:

Input programs. Input programs gather information such as the state of all subscriber lines and trunks.

Operational programs. Operational programs examine the information received and decide what, if any, output actions are required.

Subroutines. Subroutines contain data on translations of dialed digits, and trunks and network paths for the use of output programs.

Output programs. Output programs make and release connections in the switching network and operate relays in the trunk circuits.

Executive control program. The executive control program determines when each of the above programs are to be called into operation.

During a call, each of the first four programs assumes and relinquishes direction over central control in accordance with a schedule governed by the executive control program. In order to assist this process, use is made of the call store as a clearing house of information between these four functional groups. The call store is divided into various sections, each with a number of memory slots. Information is deposited and withdrawn as needed from the temporary memory stores in the call store. They are called *registers*, *hoppers*, and *buffers* in accordance with their functions. Each call being processed has one or more registers associated with it. The input programs fill the hoppers with information that is processed by the operational programs. The buffers are stocked with data by the operational programs and the subroutines for use by the output programs. The processing of any call, consequently, entails a constant interchange of data between the program store and the call store.

Line Scanning Operations in No. 1 ESS

Lifting the handset signals the origination of a call for electronic as well as electromechanical signaling systems but from that point on the operations involved in processing a call in the No. 1 ESS are entirely different and not analogous to electromechanical systems. For instance, in the S × S and crossbar central offices, a line (L) relay is associated with every subscriber line. This relay operates whenever the handset is lifted to initiate a call. Its operation starts the electromechanical switching process. In the No. 1 ESS there are no line relays. Instead, each subscriber line is connected to a ferrod sensor, a saturable ferrite-core transformer which is composed of a rectangular ferrite stick surrounded by four windings. Two windings are connected in a balanced circuit to each T and R conductor of the sub-

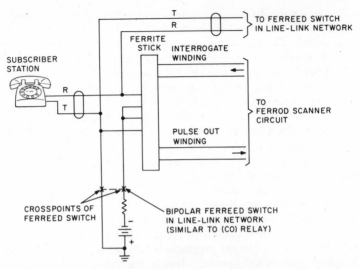

Figure 10-8   Subscriber-Line Ferrod Sensor in No. 1 ESS

scriber lines. The other two windings connect to the ferrod scanning circuit as shown in Fig. 10-8.

The ferrod sensor indicates the state of its subscriber line, that is, whether it is on-hook or off-hook. If the subscriber handset is on-hook, no current will flow in the line conductors. Therefore, a current pulse applied to one winding of the ferrod sensor will produce a corresponding pulse in the other winding. When the handset is off-hook, as in originating a call, current will flow in the line conductors and the ferrite stick of the ferrod sensor will become saturated. In this case, when a current pulse is applied to the "in-

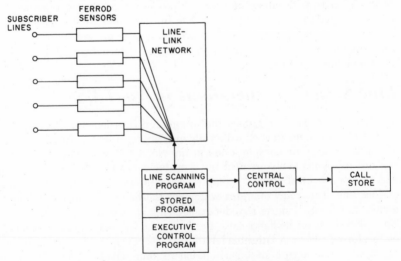

Figure 10-9   Line Scanning Process

terrogate" winding from the ferrod scanner circuit, the ferrite core already will be saturated. This condition will prevent the generation of an output pulse in the "pulse out" winding, thereby denoting an off-hook state. Thus, the on-hook and off-hook states are indicated, respectively, by the absence or presence of current flow in the T and R conductors of the subscriber line.

The battery supply for the balanced winding of each ferrod sensor is controlled by the crosspoint contacts of a bipolar ferreed switch on the line-link network. This ferreed switch is operated on originating calls to connect the calling subscriber line to the line-link network for subsequent connection to service or other trunks. Similarly, on incoming calls, the ferreed switch functions like the crosspoints of a crossbar switch to connect the line-link network to the called line. Thus, the ferreed switch may be considered to function in a similar fashion as the cut-off (CO) relay in electromechanical switching systems.

The ferrod sensors of all subscriber lines are scanned at least once every 200 milliseconds by central control as directed by the line scanning program (see Fig. 10-9). The "present" state of the line is reported to central control by the line scanning program and the "last" state by the memory in call store. Whenever a change of state of any subscriber line is found by central control, the line scanning program temporarily stops the scanning action. At the same time, the equipment number of the particular line on the line-link network is recorded in call store denoting, for example, the start of a call. The action initiated on one line is completed before the next line is scanned. When all ferrod sensors have been scanned, the line scanning program returns control to the executive control program.

State of Line Logic Operations

The logic circuits enable central control to determine whether or not a change of state has occurred in any subscriber line. Suppose that central control checks the condition or state of line 6789 and has requested reports from the line scanning program and the memory in call store concerning the line's respective "present" and "last" state. Recall that a binary 0 digit can represent zero voltage or no-pulse output, and that a binary 1 can indicate a voltage or pulse output. If line 6789 is on-hook, its ferrod sensor when scanned will produce a pulse. This action will cause a 1 bit to be sent back to central control. If this line should be off-hook, no pulse would be generated during the scanning process, transmitting a 0 bit to central control as an indication of the line's "present" state. Concurrently, the call store memory will be advising central control of the "last" state of line 6789.

The "present" and "last" conditions of line 6789 are simultaneously received by the logic circuit in central control as shown in Fig. 10-10. This logic circuit comprises AND, OR, and NOT gates. If both the "present" and "last" states are represented by bits 0 or 1, the output signal in central control will be 0, signifying that the condition of line 6789 has not changed since the last scan. However, if there has been a change, the output signal in central control will be 1.

Subscriber Line Conditions and Resultant Binary Signals

Line Scanning Program Present State	Call Store Last State	Central Control Output Signal	Meaning
1	1	0	State not changed. Line not in use. **(on-hook)**
0	1	1	State changed. Call initiated. **(off-hook)**
0	0	0	State not changed. Subscriber talking. **(off-hook)**
1	0	1	State changed. Call completed. **(on-hook)**

Figure 10-10

Assume that a call is being originated by line 6789. The off-hook condition will cause current to flow in the line and its ferrod sensor will not return a pulse when scanned for its "present" state. This will cause a 1 bit to be transmitted to the logic in central control. The essential elements of this logic are four electronic gates, OR, AND #1, NOT, and AND #2 as shown in Fig. 10-11. First, the ferrod line scanner reports on the "present" state of 6789 by sending a 1 bit as mentioned above. At the same time, the call store memory advises that the "last" state was 0 (on-hook condition). Bits 1 and 0 are now applied in parallel to the respective inputs of gates OR and AND #1. Since an OR gate will produce an output signal only when any one or more of its input circuits are energized, the output of OR will be 1 in this instance. On the other hand, pulses must appear simultaneously on all of its input leads for an AND gate to produce an output pulse. Since

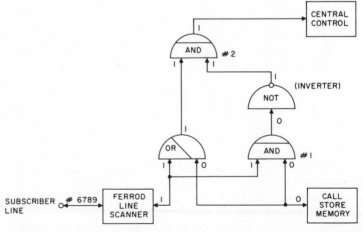

Figure 10-11   Logic Circuit for Indicating "Present" and "Last" States

AND #1 has a 0 and 1 input, its output will be 0. The NOT gate may be considered an inverted amplifier. Therefore, the 0 bit from AND #1 will become a 1 at the input to AND #2. Because both inputs to AND #2 are 1, an output pulse will be produced and 1 will be sent to central control as an indication that a change of state has occurred in line 6789.

As another example, suppose that the "present" and "last" states of line 6789 are the same, namely, on-hook. The inputs to gates OR and AND #1 in this event will be 0 from both the line scanner and call store memory. The outputs of gates OR and AND #1 likewise will be 0. The NOT gate will invert the 0 from AND #1 to a 1 for connection to an input of AND #2. However, since the other input to AND #2 (from OR) is 0, the output of AND #2 also will be 0. This 0 signal will serve to inform central control that the state of line 6789 has not changed.

Central Control

The most important role in the processing of a call is played by central control. It is a binary digital and computing instrument of the synchronous type that performs very complex actions, one at a time. Clock pulses generated from a 2-MHz crystal oscillator, which provides cycles of 5.5 microseconds, govern its stepping from one cycle of operations to the next. Because of its complexity and the very high reliability requirements, the entire control unit of the No. 1 ESS is duplicated. That is, there are two units of central control, program store and call store. The two central controls actually process all data and operations simultaneously and the results are compared at key points in the No. 1 ESS to check against any errors.

Understanding the operations of central control and its associated program store and call store would require a comprehensive knowledge of data processing and computer engineering. These explanations are outside the field of this book so that it only will be practical to summarize the principal actions performed. Three major classes of instructions are received by central control. The first comprises orders to sense the state or condition of lines or trunks. For example, central control may be directed to examine the ferrod line scanning circuits associated with subscriber lines to detect requests for service, as indicated by a change of state. This scanning operation serves to detect inputs to central control.

A second class of instructions processes the input data. In this case, central control may process the input data, deposit the results temporarily in call store, and later recall them when they are needed. Additional data may be subsequently obtained from program store. These operations do not necessarily progress from one step to the next in sequence. Central control, on encountering certain conditions during any stage in the program, may decide to transfer to another processing action instead of continuing through the particular program.

The third class of instructions refers to outputs produced by central control which operate, for example, relays in trunk circuits and close ferreed switches on line-link or trunk-link networks. In general, a single instruction controls a single operation. However, individual instructions can be combined in various ways as required for control purposes.

Central control processes instructions by first requesting information from program store and call store. In this respect, it may obtain service requests from call store and then ask for processing instructions that are stored at a particular address in program store. In return, program store may send certain instructions to central control that were previously deposited at that address. One part of the instruction tells central control what to do with the information being processed and the address in the second part of the instruction tells where to do it.

Transmission of data and control signals between central control and other units of the No. 1 ESS is handled over a peripheral bus system which is a special multipair cable that interconnects the major subsystem elements used in processing calls. Figure 10-12 is an elementary representation of the peripheral bus arrangement. Note that 2 to 6 program store units and up to 14 call store units may be provided depending upon the size of the particular No. 1 ESS central office.

Memory Devices

The memory devices in the No. 1 ESS are designed to store a bit in a specific location and to recall it on command. Millions of bits can be stored in a single memory and some bits may be stored for years and recalled as often as needed. Other bits may be recalled within a few microseconds. Both the permanent magnet twister memory used in program store and the ferrite sheet memory employed in call store comprise magnetic cores.

A bistable ferrite material of uniform composition is used for the mag-

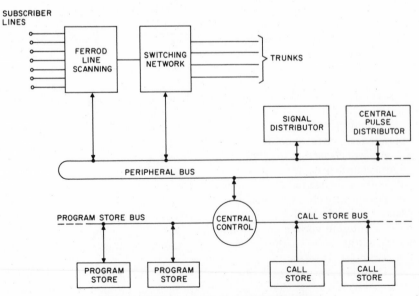

Figure 10-12   Peripheral Bus System

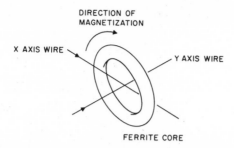

Figure 10-13 Diagram of a Memory Cell

net core of a memory cell. Its main magnetic characteristic is a square-loop magnetization or hysteresis curve. Thousands of such cores are assembled in a coordinate frame of wires to form the memory. Each ferrite core has two wires which intersect at right-angles to each other, that is, in the X and Y directions. The core can be magnetized in either a clockwise or counterclockwise direction by passing a sufficient current through these wires in the proper direction. Clockwise magnetization of the core represents a binary 0 digit, and counterclockwise magnetization, a binary 1. Figure 10-13 shows a memory cell in its simplest form.

To store or "write" a binary digit into the core memory necessitates that current be sent through the X and Y wires in the proper direction. This is accomplished by applying half of the current value needed to switch or change the magnetization of the core to the X wire. The other half of the current value is put on the Y wire. The current in each wire, therefore, is less than that needed to change the core's magnetization; that is, from clockwise to counterclockwise or vice-versa. Moreover, the magnetization of a core will not be changed if only one of the wires passing through it carries current. The result is that only the particular ferrite core at the intersection of the current carrying X and Y wires will be magnetized in either a clockwise or counterclockwise direction. This core then will remain magnetized without further application of current.

The same current values are applied to the ferrite core memory cell to read-out the binary digit that had been stored. As an example, assume that the core already is magnetized in a clockwise direction. Now, if the applied currents also tend to magnetize the core in that same direction, the core's magnetization will not be changed. However, if the core has been magnetized in a counterclockwise direction, the applied currents will cause a change in the core's flux. This reversal of the magnetic flux will induce a voltage pulse in the "sense" wire which is used to read-out the memory. A read-out of the memory, in effect, consists of sensing these resultant voltage and no-voltage patterns.

The ferrite sheet memory used in call store is of modular construction. Each module contains 192 separate ferrite sheets arranged in three adjacent stacks of 64 sheets. Four such modules comprise one call store. A single ferrite sheet contains 256 holes on a 16 by 16 grid. The material surrounding each hole is a memory cell. It is similar to the single core memory cell. The X,

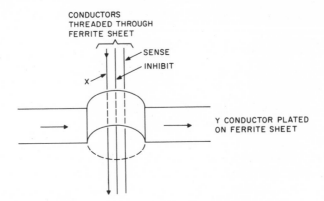

CONDUCTORS
THREADED THROUGH
FERRITE SHEET

SENSE

INHIBIT

X

Y CONDUCTOR PLATED
ON FERRITE SHEET

Figure 10-14   Ferrite Sheet Memory Cell

"inhibit," and "sense" wires are run through all 64 sheets in each stack of the module. The Y wires are formed by interconnecting plated conductors on three ferrite sheets on each level of the module. Figure 10-14 shows a typical memory cell on a ferrite sheet.

Figure 10-15   Memory Card in Program Store
courtesy of AT&T

The ferrite sheet memory in call store functions similarly to the simple core cell in the figure. In operation, the X and Y conductors carry the currents to switch the magnetization of the core material at their junction. The "inhibit" wire is utilized to prevent the memory cell from switching during the "writing" of a binary digit. For this purpose, a pulse is sent over the "inhibit" wire simultaneously with, but in the opposite direction to, the pulses over the X and Y conductors. The "sense" wire serves to read the memory by checking for voltage pulses or no pulses.

The twister memory is employed in program store. Its basic element is an aluminum card containing 2816 tiny rectangular magnetic spots of vicalloy which is a special magnetic alloy similar to that used in tape recorders. These vicalloy spots are the basic memory cells. A magnetized spot represents a binary 0 digit and an unmagnetized spot represents a binary 1. The condition of each memory cell (vicalloy magnetic spot) is sensed by a twister wire, a copper wire that has been helically wrapped with a very thin permalloy tape. The twister wire is run along under the vicalloy magnetic spots. Unlike the ferrite sheet memory in call store, the twister memory can be read an unlimited number of times. To change the stored information, it is necessary to temporarily remove the particular twister aluminum card and then magnetize or demagnetize its vicalloy spots as required. See Figs. 10-15 and 10-16.

Figure 10-16   Memory Cards in Large Memory Section
courtesy of Bell Telephone Laboratories

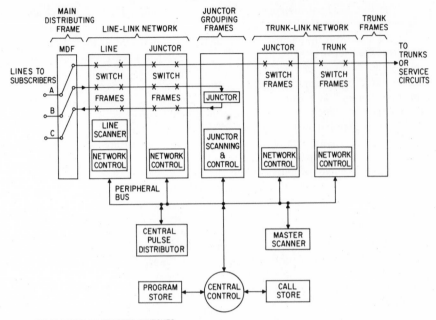

X = CROSSPOINTS OF FERREED SWITCHES.

Figure 10-17   No. 1 ESS Switching Network

No. 1 ESS Switching Network

In the S × S system, the selector switches, directly controlled by the dialed information, pick a network connection by testing the C or S leads for an idle path or trunk. In crossbar switching systems, the marker tests the S leads of various links to find a set of idle switching paths for connections. In the No. 1 ESS the ferreed switch performs all switching network connections.

The line-link and trunk-link frames comprise the switching network in the No. 1 ESS. The line-link network connects through junctors to establish paths for intraoffice, interoffice and tandem (trunk-to-trunk) calls. Intraoffice calls, however, bypass the trunk-line network by utilizing an intraoffice junctor circuit which provides talking battery and supervisory signaling on intraoffice calls. All other traffic is routed through the trunk-link network to the respective trunk and service circuits for necessary control and supervision.

Figure 10-17 shows the general arrangement of the switching network and its associated electronic processing units. An interoffice outgoing call from subscriber A, for example, would be routed through the line-link network, the junctor grouping frames and the trunk-link network to the designated outgoing trunk on the trunk frame. A local call from subscriber B to C would be connected only through the line-link network to a junctor circuit on the junctor grouping frame. These calls are illustrated in the diagram.

When fully equipped, a line-link network contains four line switch frames and four junctor switch frames. Each line switch frame incorporates the ferrod sensors and bipolar ferreed switches associated with the subscriber lines that it serves. Normally, 64 subscriber lines have access to 16 links or a 4 to 1 line concentration ratio. A total of 16 line concentrators with control circuits, ferrod line scanners and bipolar ferreed switches usually are provided to serve up to 1024 subscriber lines on each line switch frame. Therefore, one line-link network would have a capacity of 4096 lines and 1024 junctors. The crosspoints of the ferreed switches on the line switch and junctor switch frames perform all path interconnections for a call under direction of central control. Note that only two-wire paths, the T and R leads (talking circuits), are switched.

A trunk-link network usually contains four junctor switch and four trunk switch frames. The number of these frames can be increased if the traffic warrants a larger concentration ratio. For the usual 1 to 1 concentration rate, one trunk-link network will have a capacity of 1024 trunks, the same as the number of junctors. Figure 10-18 shows the general arrangement of the line-link network, junctor frames and the trunk-link network.

The switching network, with its many possible links and paths available for any call, requires some means to indicate which paths or trunks are idle and which are busy at any given time. In electromechanical switching systems, use is made of the C (control) or S (sleeve) leads as a memory device for this means. Selectors in the S × S and panel offices test these leads when hunting for idle paths. In the No. 5 Crossbar, the marker performs this function. The No. 1 ESS makes use of memory in the call store to select idle links or paths in a unique way.

Call store maintains in one area of its memory a *network map*. This

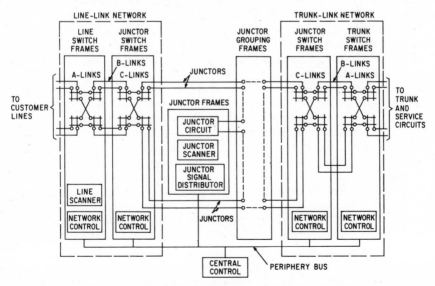

Figure 10-18   Switching Network in No. 1 ESS

network map contains a record of the idle or busy states of all links or paths in the central office. An idle state is indicated for any link or path involved in a call by the binary digit 1 and a busy state by the binary digit 0. Consequently, call store and not the switching network is consulted for idle paths in completing a call. For instance, when a call is in progress, every link or path used is identified by a group of binary digits called *path memory word* and stored in call store. These busy links are marked by the binary 0 digit in the network map of call store. When the call is disconnected and the same links become idle, they will be marked by the binary 1 in the network map. At the same time, the associated path memory word will be erased from call store. A simplified diagram, Fig. 10-19, illustrates the possible paths that may be recorded in the network map of call store on a call from subscriber A to B. A 1 indicates an idle link and 0 a busy link. Thus, there are only two idle paths available, as indicated by arrows, in this particular example.

Intraoffice Call

A brief review of how a call is handled in the No. 1 ESS will help to explain the total system more clearly. The last scan of line 6789, in an off-hook state, indicated that a call was being initiated. This information, sent by the *line scanning program*, is recorded in a line service request hopper of call store. At the same time, other information is received from program store concerning the kind of station equipment in use; that is, rotary dial or touch-tone. Assuming that line 6789 is equipped for touch-tone dialing, central control will direct the line-link and trunk-link networks to connect the line's termination to a service trunk equipped for touch-tone digit reception. Dial tone will be sent to the calling line by this service trunk.

Next, the *digit scanning program* will function and central control directs that that subscriber line be scanned at 10 millisecond intervals in order to detect and record the touch-tone pulses. These pulses are temporarily stored as input data in an assigned register in call store. No further action is taken until dialing is completed. After all digits are dialed, the program store is consulted for the next step. Central control is informed as to the type of call, intraoffice in this instance, and it will refer to the network map in call store for idle links and paths available for connection to the called line. Upon receiving this data, central control will direct the line-link to make the necessary interconnections between the calling and called line through a junctor circuit.

If the called line is busy (off-hook state), the *ringing connection program* will direct that busy tone be returned to the calling party from the junctor circuit. If the line is idle, the junctor circuit will connect ringing current and an audible ringing tone will be sent back to the calling subscriber.

When the called party answers the call, the resultant change of state is recorded by call store. Central control then directs that the calling line be scanned at the regular 200-millisecond intervals. No further action is taken until the parties disconnect. At that time, as indicated by a change

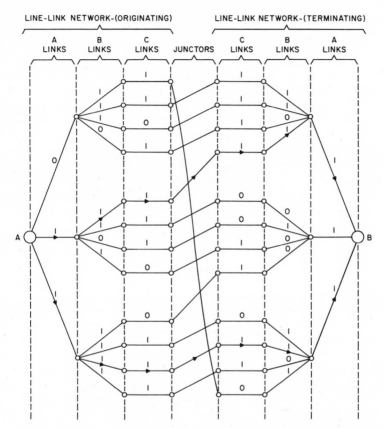

Figure 10-19 Network Map in Call Store for Intraoffice Call

of state (from off-hook to on-hook), central control will direct the line-link network to release the connections. Interoffice calls are handled in a similar manner. In this case, both the line-link and trunk-link networks are inter-connected and directed by central control to connect the calling line to an outgoing trunk. For tandem calls (trunk-to-trunk), only the trunk-link network is utilized.

Review Questions

1. What justifies the need for the great complexity in electronic switching systems? Define 8 nanoseconds.
2. What are the two principal types of electronic switching systems? How do they differ?
3. Name four or more chief elements of the Bell System's No. 1 Electronic Switching System (ESS).
4. Define memory and logic as used in electronic switching. What principal elements of the No. 1 ESS utilize memory?

5. Name three types of logic circuits used. Which one may be considered as an inverting amplifier?

6. What devices are associated with each subscriber's line in the No. 1 ESS? What are their main functions?

7. What are the two main memory devices in the No. 1 ESS and where are they used? What is their prime magnetic characteristic?

8. What happens if a core memory cell is magnetized in a clockwise direction and the applied currents tend to magnetize the core in the same direction? What is the resultant read-out?

9. What conditions in a twister memory represent binary 0 and 1 digits? How many times may a twister memory be read?

10. What unit records the idle state of all links and paths? How are the idle and busy states indicated in this unit?

Glossary

Glossary

Appearance: Locations on switch frames and switchboards of wires and equipment. For example, subscriber lines or wires appearing on a line-relay frame and the jack on a switchboard panel.

Area code: The three-digit prefix assigned to a telephone number for direct distance dialing purposes.

Attenuation: A decrease in signal magnitude when transmitting from one point to another, usually expressed as a ratio in decibels (dB).

Balanced circuit: Telephone circuit in which the two conductors are electrically balanced to each other and to ground.

Bandwidth: The difference between the limiting frequencies of a continuous frequency band.

Battery: Usually means the 48-volt storage battery in the central office. *See* Common battery *and* Talking battery.

Battery pulses: Negative potential pulses from the central office battery which are applied to a telephone circuit.

Bit: A binary digit, 0 or 1.

C lead: *See* S.

Carrier transmission: A system for transmitting many voice channels over a common telephone circuit.

CCS: Telephone traffic unit which means hundred-second calls or the total traffic in seconds divided by 100. *See* Fig. 5 - 10.

Centrex: An improved PBX system that also provides direct inward dialing (DID) and automatic number identification (ANI) of the calling PBX station.

Common battery: The nominal 48-volt storage battery in the central office used as the common battery supply to all subscriber stations and the central office switching equipment.

Cord circuit: Three-conductor (T, R, and S) cord equipped with a plug used on manual switchboards for making connections to subscriber lines and trunks.

Crosspoint: The operated contacts on a crossbar switch.

Crosstalk: Unwanted sound in a voice channel resulting from cross-coupling to another voice channel.

153

DDD: Direct distance dialing by subscribers over the nationwide intertoll telephone network.

Dry circuit: A telephone circuit carrying voice-frequency currents without the flow of dc.

DSA Switchboard: Dial system assistance switchboard. It was formerly called the "dial A board."

Electromechanical switching: Relays, selector switches, and other electromechanical devices used to perform central office switching functions.

Electronic switching: Electronic circuits and solid-state devices used to perform most central office switching functions.

End office: The local central office which interconnects subscriber lines and trunks. It is termed the Class 5 office in the DDD network.

Facsimile: Electronic transmission of photographs or documents over a telephone channel.

Far end: The terminating end of an outgoing trunk or the incoming trunk equipment in the called or terminating office.

Float-charging: Charging a storage battery at about the same rate that it is being discharged by the load.

Frequency division multiplex (FDM): The transmission of two or more signals over a common path by using a different frequency band for each signal.

Grid network: The connecting paths that comprise the crossbar common-control switching system.

Ground pulses: Positive potential pulses from the central office battery applied to a telephone circuit.

Hertz: Unit of frequency, formerly cycles per second.

High-low: Use of a marginal relay for signaling purposes in a manual switchboard cord circuit that operates on high current values, but not on low current.

Hybrid arrangement: Use of hybrid-type transformer with carrier circuits or two-wire repeaters to amplify conversations in both directions without causing feedback or "singing" effects.

Induction coil: The autotransformer used in telephone instruments as part of the transmission network.

Interoffice trunk: Telephone channel between two local central offices.

Interrupting equipment: Motor-driven mechanical devices used to break the ringing generator's output into ringing and silent periods, creating the busy and ringback tone pulses, etc.

Intraoffice trunk: The trunk or path connection within the same central office.

Jack: A three-conductor receptacle usually mounted in vertical panels of a switchboard position to accept the plug of the switchboard cord.

Jumper wire: Cross-connecting wires on an equipment frame or on the main or intermediate distributing frame of the central office.

Junctors: The connecting circuits or paths between the line-link and trunk-link frames in a No. 5 crossbar central office.

Keyshelf: Horizontal shelf of a switchboard position containing the switchboard cords, keys, and pushbuttons.

kHz: Abbreviation for kilohertz or 1000 hertz (1000 cycles per second).

Lock-up: The circuit holding a relay operated through its operated contacts after the initial operating path is disconnected.

Longitudinal currents: Currents which flow in the same direction in the two conductors of a cable pair or pair of wires.

Loop: The closed loop circuit formed by the subscribers telephone set and the cable pair and other conductors that connect it to the central office switching equipment.

Marginal relay: A relay designed to operate only on a specified current flow which is greater than the current normally flowing in the circuit.

Mark: Battery or ground potential placed on a bank terminal or on connecting wires to control switching operations in electromechanical and electronic central offices.

MHz: Abbreviation for megahertz or 1,000,000 hertz (1,000,000 cycles per second).

Mobile telephone service: Radiotelephone service provided to motor vehicles, railroad trains and airplanes.

Multifrequency tones: Signaling code utilizing pairs of frequencies in the 700 - 1700-Hz range.

Multiplex: *See* Carrier transmission.

Nanosecond: One billionth of a second (10^{-9}).

Near-end: The originating end of a trunk circuit or connecting path.

Negative resistance battery: The potential at a resistance which connects to the central office battery.

No-busy test: A circuit used to connect to a busy subscriber's line number.

Normally closed contacts: The closed contacts on an unoperated relay.

Normally released contacts: The open contacts on an unoperated relay.

Off-hook: Circuit condition caused when the handset is lifted from the switchhook of the telephone set.

Office code: The first three digits of the seven-digit telephone number assigned to a subscriber.

On-hook: The normal circuit condition when the handset is on the switchhook of the telephone set.

PBX, PABX: Private automatic branch exchange.

Peripheral bus: A special multipair cable that interconnects the major subsystem elements in an electronic switching office of the No. 1 ESS type.

Polar relay: A relay with a permanent-magnet core that is designed to operate only when the current is flowing in the proper direction.

Primary Center: A toll switching center designated Class 3 office in the DDD or intertoll network.

Primary winding: The principal operating winding of a relay. The winding of a transformer connected to the source of the a-c supply.

R: Designates the ring side of the conductors of a cable pair or two-wire telephone circuit.

Receiver: The electromagnetic unit in the telephone handset used to convert electrical energy to sound energy.

Regional center: The main switching center of Class 1 office in the DDD or intertoll network.

Repeating coil: A transformer with split and balanced primary and secondary windings.

Retard coil: An audio-frequency choke coil used to limit the flow of voice-frequency currents in a telephone circuit.

Reverse battery: Reversal of the normal potential on a trunk to indicate that the called party has answered.

Revertive pulse: Ground pulses sent back to the sender in the originating panel office from the various selector frames to control the selection process.

Ringer: The bell unit in the subscriber's telephone set.

Ringing current: 20-Hz ac at a voltage of 75-105 supplied by the central office to ring the subscriber's bell.

S: Designates the sleeve or control leads in electromechanical central offices which are used to make-busy circuits, trunks and subscriber lines, as well as to test for busy conditions. It also designates the sleeve wire on a switchboard cord.

Secondary winding: The minor winding on a relay having two windings. The winding on a transformer that is not connected to the a-c source.

Sectional Center: The Class 2 switching office in the DDD or intertoll network.

Slow-release relay: A relay with a copper sleeve over one end of its core causing it to be slow in releasing.

Solid state: Use of semiconductor devices, such as transistors and diodes, in electronic circuits.

Subset: The subscriber's telephone instrument.

T: Designates the tip side of the conductors of a cable pair or two-wire telephone circuit.

Talking battery: The dc supplied by the central office battery to the subscriber's loop for the operation of the carbon transmitter in the handset.

Talking path: The transmission path which comprises the T and R conductors or leads of a telephone circuit.

Tertiary winding: The third winding on a polar relay used for the bias voltage.

Time division multiplex: The process of transmitting two or more signals over a common path by using different time intervals for each signal.

Timed release circuit: A circuit designed to automatically release other connected circuits after a preset interval.

Tone alternator: Motor-driven a-c generator that produces audio-frequency tones.

Transmitter: The carbon device in the telephone handset used to convert speech to electrical energy.

Trunk: A telephone circuit or channel between two central offices or switching equipments.

Wet trunk: A trunk circuit in which d-c flows in the T and R conductors or the transmission loop.

Index